BEANBALL

BEANBALL

Tom Seaver with Herb Resnicow

William Morrow and Company, Inc.

New York

Library of Congress Cataloging-in-Publication Data

Seaver, Tom, 1944–
  Beanball.

  I. Resnicow, Herb. II. Title.
PS3569.E225B44   1989   813'.54   88-8237
ISBN 0-688-07194-5

Printed in the United States of America

First Edition

1   2   3   4   5   6   7   8   9   10
BOOK DESIGN BY BRIAN MOLLOY

To Harvey Haddix, Rube Walker, Bill Fischer, and Dave Duncan for twenty years of help

—TOM SEAVER

To those future Tom Seavers, my grandsons Daniel Ilan Resnicow and Joel Ethan Resnicow

—HERB RESNICOW

1

Meditations by Marcus Aurelius Burr

This afternoon, in a hard-fought contest, the Brooklyn Bandits barely beat out the Denver Rockies for the National League Championship, and Samuel Moultran Prager finally bought the pennant he'd been trying to get for the past five years, ever since the Bandits and the Rockies were organized to even out the number of teams in the two major leagues. Playboy Prager is known as Sonny to his few friends, but as Slippery Sam to the rest of the world.

The trouble with Slippery Sam's brilliant approach to putting together a winner—the other owners should have recognized this on sight—is Prager himself. Anyone with half a brain would realize that after you hire one of the best managers in baseball, Enzo (Butch) Bello, and give him a five-year, multimillion-dollar contract, you leave him alone. You don't tell him how to manage and you don't criticize him in the papers or in front of the players. You also give him a vote as to which players to buy and which to sell.

What does a manager do with four great outfielders—all higher paid than the manager—who complain to the owner if they're not played every day (and not as pinch hitters either)? What does a manager do with four star pitchers, all lefties, each demanding to pitch every five days, insisting that otherwise he'll lose his edge? What does a manager do with a sore-armed ex-fastballer in the last year of his no-cut-no-trade million-dollar-per-year contract who has turned forty, suddenly decided he's a knuckleball pitcher, and just wants to relieve, when the only other right-handed starter is on the disabled list? What does a manager do with two shortstops, when one can't hit and the other can't field?

Slippery Sam inherited a lot of play money, but money alone sure as hell doesn't make a baseball team work. I have the feeling Bello has decided that Prager can go to hell—which is a pity because the Bandits are a potentially great team—and that instead of doing what he knows is best, will follow the owner's orders to the letter, keeping a copy of each little note Prager sends down to him as evidence of who's responsible for what.

So I offer my prediction: The Bandits will lose and the Boomers will again be the World's Champs. Four straight. New Jersey fans should send a carload of roses to Slippery Sam Prager, without whom none of this would have been possible.

Sports editor Julius Witter moved the stack of papers aside and laid the computer printout of Marc's column carefully on his desk. He moved the sheets so they were precisely six inches from the edge of the desk and six inches from the right side, then ostentatiously adjusted the pack one millimeter each way. Marc bit the inside of his cheek as Witter started his rejection routine, but said nothing. Witter ran his right thumb over both halves of his pepper-and-salt military moustache and pulled the worn gray cardigan straight over his long, thin body. He put both big feet on the chair that he kept to the right of his desk as a footrest, pushed his reading glasses back on his bald head, focused his eyes a foot over the top of Marc's limp brown hair so he could watch the rest of the newsroom through the glass partition surrounding his office, and sighed sadly.

"You can't imagine, Burr," Witter said, choosing his words carefully, "what a thrill it gives this tired old heart to realize that after only fifteen years of my patient tutelage, you are finally beginning to understand the rudiments of communicating to the readers of *The Daily Sentry* by means of the written word."

"You're not going to edit it?" Marc asked. "It's that good?"

"There's no need to edit it, much as it needs judicious cutting and smoothing out. Now that you've written it, I suggest you read it—a useful practice that will help keep you out of trouble."

"I've read it; it's exactly what I want to say and what I've wanted to say ever since I first met Slippery Sam Prager."

"You want to use the column in lieu of intensive therapy, Burr? Or is it pure, unadulterated death wish? The situation can get worse, you know; after you're fired, you won't be able to afford the counseling you require. You will sink lower and lower until—"

"You would fire me for telling the truth, Julius?"

"Yes, I would fire you. Not for telling the truth—which may be occasionally permissible, if not overdone—but for terminal stupidity." Witter took his time filling his old black pipe, lighted it, and blew a big puff of smoke directly at Marc. "Who pays your extortionate salary, Burr?"

Marc moved back out of range of Witter's chemical warfare. "The faithful readers of *The Daily Sentry* pay my salary, sir, the ones who carefully skip the rest of the garbage in the paper to get to my column." He took his wire-rimmed glasses and put them in his shirt pocket, ready for a fight. "I read the survey that showed the first thing thirty-eight percent of our readers turned to in the morning was my column."

"That survey was not intended for your eyes—when I find out who leaked it, she will be fired too—because I knew you would misinterpret it. Our faithful readers turn to your column because your ineptness makes them feel superior and the news on our front page is too horrible to start a day with. In fact, most of our readers don't read *The Sentry* for the news at all; they're interested only in the sports section and choose us because we're a tabloid, small enough to read on the subway comfortably. And you're wrong, as usual, Burr, about who pays you. You don't see readers' names on the bottom of your paycheck, you see Mr. Heisenberg's. Our readers have nothing to do with your continued eating.''

"You're kidding, Julius. Heisenberg would cut staff if we lost one reader. Hell, he'd cut staff if one reader wrote in to complain. About anything.''

"True. Fortunately for you our readers are functionally illiterate—which is why your pretentious prose fits their needs exactly—and would never think of writing anything voluntarily, much less a letter to a newspaper. However, Mr. Heisenberg is preternaturally sensitive to complaints from advertisers, friends of advertisers, and anyone who is rich. Of which description, every category fits the honorable owner of the Brooklyn Bandits perfectly.''

"Slippery Sam can't complain; everything I said is true.''

"He can complain, he will complain, and I will finally get orders—not permission, Burr, *orders*—from Mr. Heisenberg to dismiss you for cause.'' He smiled in anticipation. "Normally I would welcome the opportunity to free myself of an irritation, of a bone in my throat, but having invested all this time in you, having given you a column, and having allowed you some credit for writing the Super Bowl murder story, it would be somewhat embarrassing for me to get rid of you so soon after.''

"I was the one who solved the Super Bowl murder and you wrote the story under your byline, Julius, with a tiny credit for me as a researcher.''

"Perfectly accurate, Burr, since I did write the story. You were hardly in a position to move your lips, much less operate a word processor. I think it was extremely generous of me to even mention your name. Haven't I shown my innate benevolence and gratitude by suppressing my natural and proper desire to be done with you once and for all, by bringing you in here and giving you an undeserved final opportunity to retract this libelous column?''

"You're going to censor me? You want me to pull this column? You'd really fire me for writing this?''

10

"Even if Mr. Prager did not call Mr. Heisenberg to complain, which is extremely doubtful, he would certainly call me to explain why, just before World Series time, no *Sentry* reporter would be allowed into the Gruber Dome or any other stadium the Bandits happen to be in, even if they bought tickets, and why no one connected with the Bandits would be allowed to speak with anyone from *The Sentry*, now and forever. Under those circumstances I would not wait for Mr. Heisenberg to fire me for not dismissing you at once; I would fire you immediately."

Marc digested this. It was bitter, but coupled with the exhilaration he had felt as he was writing the column was the knowledge that it had a very small chance of seeing print. Other papers never interfered with their columnists; the function of a column was to allow its writer to speak his mind, and the readers liked it that way. But other papers did not have an owner as penny-pinching, as sensitive to the loss of advertising, as inconsiderate of the welfare of his employees, and as dictatorial, impulsive, and unpredictable as Mr. Warner Heisenberg. Marc decided to give it one last try. "Are you going to refuse to print this column, Julius? Are you going to force me to take this to the Guild?"

"Did I say that? Did I? In fact, Burr, if that column remains on my desk one more minute, I will not only print it, I will print it as it is, unedited, on the back page, where it cannot fail to come to the attention of even a Samuel Moultran Prager." He puffed smoke toward Burr again, clearly trying to reach him. Marc moved back even faster. "Tell me, Burr"—Witter sounded suspiciously fatherly—"how is Dahliah doing? Gotten a raise yet?"

"You know very well that professors get raises only once a year," Marc said bitterly. "If then." Witter said nothing, just smiled, waiting. Marc broke first. "All right," he said through clenched teeth, his normally mild face red, "what do you want me to write about that's safe?"

Witter widened his smile. "Need you ask? There are several good stories any competent reporter would latch on to immediately: the relationship of the star outfielders to each other, the competition at shortstop, the preponderance of lefty starting pitchers, Warren Lamburt's change into a knuckleball pitcher, or anything else your little heart desires. Take your choice, Burr; you're a columnist and we don't censor anybody on *The Sentry.*"

"I'll write one on Lamburt," Marc said.

"Excellent choice." Witter beamed. "I'm proud of you, Marc; you're beginning to show good newsman's judgment. May I now remind you that you're still a reporter and should really be down at the Gruber Dome getting some more fascinating stories? And in Hague Stadium. On *The Sentry,* a columnist is first and foremost a reporter. Who produces a lot of stories. So we don't have to hire more warm bodies than are absolutely necessary."

"I already wrote the story of the game. It's on your desk somewhere, under the pile."

"I'll put it into good English. What about a story from the Jersey Boomers' point of view?"

"How could I get to Jersey in time? I had to wait for the end of the Bandits' game."

"If your phone is broken, I'm sure Nelda Shaver will let you use the one in "The Sporting Woman" section. In her own private office. She really admires you, Burr, in her own inimitable way, and has often asked that you—"

"Are you threatening to assign me to work under her? All she's got on her mind is—"

"Some would consider that an opportunity; she's still a beautiful . . . Just reminding you that I'm holding five hundred words open for a phone interview with Dan Zarik on how he feels about playing against the Bandits in the World Series."

"I could write that without calling him. What he'll say will be unprintable."

"Nevertheless, we do not misquote anyone unless we try to call him, at least."

Marc picked up the printout. "You'll regret this, Julius," he promised. "One of these days, the opportunity will arise for me to—"

12

"Don't hold your breath, Burr." Witter put down his pipe. "As for that column—please build it up to seven hundred words; the one you so wisely discarded was a bit short."

"Yes, Mr. Witter, sir."

"And hand it in on time. We go to press in an hour."

"Yes, sir, Mr. Witter, sir. On time." He slammed the door behind him. The glass rattled. As usual.

2

Behind the batting-practice barrier, Warren Lamburt went into a full windup and pitched at three-quarters speed toward Jerry Leach, the third-string catcher. The clean white baseball floated in at waist height, and Pancho Rivera, the little second-string shortstop at bat, timing his swing perfectly, smashed it into the middle of the left-field bleachers of the Gruber Dome. Lamburt watched the flight of the ball and, when he turned back, saw Verne Sullivan, the pitching coach, standing on the first base line, waving him in.

"What the hell do you think you're doing out there, Lamburt?" Sullivan asked, when the pitcher reached the baseline. "You trying to build up Pancho's confidence or something? He hasn't hit one that far since he played in Caracas. I just put him there to give you a right-handed target."

"The ball had rotation," Lamburt said glumly. "So it went straight. It wasn't bouncing around."

"The ball spun, so it went straight," Sullivan mimicked him. "Gee, thanks for telling me the theory of the top-secret knuckleball pitch. Without you telling me, I never would have known how to throw a knuckleball that don't work."

"It's because I don't get enough chance to practice, Verne. On the knuckleball, I mean. When it's working right, even I can't tell where it's going and nobody can hit it. Nobody."

"I didn't call you in to argue. Butch wants to see you. With me. Now. Let's go."

14

Lamburt started walking toward the dugout, to the tunnel under the stands that led to the locker room, when Sullivan stopped him and pointed to the farthest tunnel near the right-field line. "He wants to see you *now*."

"But I haven't showered yet," Lamburt complained. He took off his cap and wiped his sleeve across his thinning blond hair, his six-one and 210-pound frame dwarfing the slim, gray-haired pitching coach walking beside him. "And I'm tired, too. Calling a fundamentals drill the morning after we won the pennant? And calling another practice for this afternoon? Butch is crazy, you know that? The past month's been murder, and the playoffs took a lot out of everybody. We should've been given a day off to celebrate with our families."

Sullivan stopped at the entrance to the tunnel and lifted his face up to Lamburt's. "You that perfect on pickoffs, Lamburt, or bunt plays, that you don't need any work? With that fat belly of yours, you'd be lucky to be able to bend over far enough to field a bunt if it came right at you."

"I'm not fat," Lamburt protested. "I'm just big all over. Besides, Fat Freddie Fitzsimmons had twice my waist, and he was the best-fielding pitcher of his day."

"Great logic, Lamburt," Sullivan said sarcastically. "So all you got to do is stuff yourself for the next two days and if you can put six inches on your waist by Saturday, we don't have to worry about the Boomers' bunting, right?"

Lamburt didn't answer.

"Or stealing or hit-and-run or anything, right?" Sullivan went on, twisting the knife, but Lamburt was too tired to rise to the bait. "I don't want to hear any bullshit, Lamburt. What I really want is for you to drop one pound—that's all, just one pound—by the time of the first game. To see if you can do it. And I'm going to weigh you today, just to make sure."

"Are you kidding, Verne? In two days? How the hell can I lose a pound that fast?"

"By not swallowing all that crap you push in your face after every practice. I'm not kidding, Lamburt; you're gonna eat nothing but steak and salad—lean steak—between now and the last game of the Series."

"Does that mean you're going to start me in the Series? That's crazy, Verne; I'm not really a starter anymore, I'm a reliever. I can go good for two, maybe three innings, but I can't go nine. Or even five. Not unless you let me use my knuckler. I can throw a knuckler all day long without hurting my arm. I bet I could even pitch a doubleheader if I threw nothing but knuckleballs."

"The manager decides who's going to start, not you. So shut up and when we get in his office, just listen to what Butch says and do it. OK?"

Warren Lamburt nodded wearily. "What kind of mood is he in?"

"What the hell do you expect, with his only healthy right-hander saying he's too weak to pitch?"

"Don't blame me for that. Prager was the guy who bought four lefties. Butch should have stopped that dead."

"Prager owns the team. How do you stop him?"

"Before you sign the contract—that's the time to get what you want."

"Not everybody's as rich as you are, Lamburt; don't rub it in."

"You didn't have to sign with Prager either, Verne. You were already retired and you knew what a bastard he is."

"Butch is too straight for his own good; somebody had to protect him from Prager. And from guys like you, too, you and the rest of those swell-headed goldbricks. One of these days I'm going to straighten you out, all of you, Prager included. You think Butch is tough? Wait till you see me in action."

"Come on, Verne, I always give it my best shot."

"That's what you think. You don't know what you're really capable of until the chips are down. If I had you under me in the marines . . ." He smiled grimly. "If I really got on your ass, Lamburt, you'd be surprised what you could do." He turned and walked briskly down the tunnel to the door of the manager's office, Lamburt taking the ten paces as slowly as possible, a march to the

16

scaffold. Sullivan turned left into the shallow recess in the wall and, just before he knocked, whispered, "Keep your mouth shut, Lamburt, and just nod your head when we get in there."

Butch Bello's office was as plain and simple as the man who occupied it. On the wall behind his desk were framed photographs of the teams he had played on, including three pennant winners and the World Series Championship team of twenty years before. Even the mementos of these prestigious events were not emphasized in any way, just lined up in chronological order with the rest of the pictures. There were no photos of owners or officials or politicians or individual athletes, not even of Butch himself, who had been voted Most Valuable Player three times in his career. The message got across to his stars real fast: It was the team that counted, not any single player. The pitcher didn't win the game, the team did. You could hit a homer in the last of the ninth with two out and bases loaded and Butch would say, "*We* won."

Bello himself, with his sloped-back forehead, mashed-in nose, dark lumpy brows, and belligerent jaw, could have passed for an ordinary ex-pug in any waterfront bar. Although he was a full six feet tall, his broad body, overhung belly, and short bandy legs gave him the look of a squashed ape. His long arms, with the huge knotted hands at their ends, did nothing to soften the image. Butch's voice, as was so often the case with big, tense, former athletes, was tight and high-pitched. In spite of this choked tenor, back in the days when he was the best catcher in the majors, his chatter from behind the plate was clearly understood in the bleachers, and his screaming at the umpire was often heard outside the ballpark.

"I'll explain it to you one more time, Lamburt," Bello was saying relatively softly, so that his words could have been heard only by someone in the reception room outside. "You want to be manager, you go to Prager right now and tell him. Until then, I'm paid to manage and you're paid to pitch. You pitch when I tell you and how I tell you and what I tell you, and no back talk. And what I'm telling you is, you're going to be a starter in the Series, even if

I gotta personally break both your legs." Verne Sullivan made smoothing motions with his hands, trying to soften the manager's rage.

"I'm not telling you how to manage, Butch," Warren Lamburt said earnestly, looking straight into Bello's angry dark eyes. "All I'm trying to do is explain why I shouldn't start a game. For the benefit of the team. Listen to me and then, if you think I'm wrong, I'll do it your way. But I got to warn you, any game I start, we'll probably lose."

"You telling me you're not going to *try*? You're going to *throw* a game?" Bello's scream shook the paneled walls of the office. He stood up and started around his desk, his huge hands reaching out for Lamburt.

"No, no—stop!" the pitcher yelled, jumping toward the door, as Sullivan threw his body in front of Bello's charge. "I never even thought of that. All I meant was . . . Just listen, will you? Listen to me?"

As Sullivan, with surprising strength, pushed Bello back behind the desk, Lamburt took his chair again. "Take it easy, Butch," Sullivan said. "He didn't mean it that way. If you slug him, he won't be able to pitch at all and Prager will have your hide." Bello finally sat down, his face red as he glared at Lamburt.

"Talk fast, Lamburt," Verne Sullivan said, "and it better be good. And just so you know where I stand, I want you to start at least one game in the Series too."

"I don't have the pop on my fastball anymore." Lamburt explained. "I knew I would lose it eventually and I prepared for it. Summers, when everybody else was loafing, I was practicing. I looked around at who was pitching at forty and it was people like Niekro and Perry. No way was I going to throw spitters, so I figured I had to develop a good knuckleball like Niekro."

"You still got a decent fastball," Sullivan interrupted. "I seen you when you thought nobody was looking."

"For an occasional pitch, to throw their timing off, yeah, I could still do it, five or six times in a game. But if I had to throw the regular way, fastballs and curves and sliders and sinkers, my arm would go in two innings. Knuckleballs, they don't take anything out of you. I could throw them all day long if you'd let me. You want me to start, let me throw my knuckler. Every pitch.''

"Nothing but knucklers?" Sullivan said incredulously. "Against the Boomers? Are you crazy? If they knew what was coming, they'd tee off on you like batting practice.''

"No they wouldn't, Verne. If I don't know how a knuckler is going to move, how is the batter going to?"

"And that's another thing, Lamburt." Bello got back into the conversation. "You and that stupid knuckleball—nobody can catch it. Half the time the catcher's got to grab it barehanded. You already split Walt Krumanski's finger with that dumb pitch in practice. I'll be lucky if he can start by the third game.''

"That's because he isn't used to . . . I need a catcher to practice with steady. It's very hard to get any control if I don't practice every day and Verne won't give me anyone to catch for me.''

"You can have all the catching you need," Sullivan retorted, "if you'll stick to pitching regular. I only got two catchers left and I can't afford to lose another one right before the Series. You want to throw a knuckler once in a while, like a change-up, OK, but I'm not going to let you use nothing but a knuckleball in a Series game; your control with it is just too lousy. You'd walk in ten runs an inning.''

"My control is good if I can practice throwing it every day. Give me Jerry Leach—you're not going to let him start anyway—for this afternoon and the next three days, and I'll be ready to start Game Three. With Krumanski.''

"You trying to tell me the rotation?" Sullivan attempted to keep his voice level. "I'm the only coach in the majors with six starters and only three relievers in the bullpen. All season long I've been juggling the rotation, trying to give each starter enough work to keep his edge—with damn little cooperation from you, Lamburt— and not put in too many lefties in a row against the same team. Every one of them's gone running to Prager, crying to Prager, and that moron gets on Butch and screws up the whole setup. On top of everything, Lebko twists his knee. . . . I've had it, Lamburt. So help me, the next guy who gives me a hard time . . .''

"I've heard enough of this horseshit," Bello said decisively, "And I don't want to hear no more. I'm gonna explain it to you one more time—that's all, Lamburt, just once—and then you're going to go out and do what Verne says." He drew a deep breath. "I got five starting pitchers, Lamburt. Five. The four big-headed stars Prager saddled me with, all lefties, plus you. You're the only right-handed starter I got left, OK? The Boomers are the best-slugging team of all time. They got four men with a hundred runs batted in and three of them are righties. They're tougher than any team we got in the National League and I need every little edge I can get to have any kind of chance of beating them. So I got to start a right-handed pitcher against them righties as much as I could. That means you. The only way I can be sure of getting you in there twice is for you to start the first game. OK? And I don't want you talking about this to nobody, not even your wife. You're going to surprise the Boomers, and you're going to beat them. OK? That's it. Now get out. I got to meet with Prager in fifteen minutes and I don't need any more problems than what I already got."

Sullivan and Lamburt got up. Lamburt couldn't resist speaking. "I understand what you're saying, Butch, but the problem is I can't throw hard for even one game, much less two. My arm will go completely. Forever."

Butch Bello stood up too, and leaned on his desk, his jaw six inches from the pitcher's face. "I've had it with you goddamn overpaid prima donnas," he screamed, "right up to here. So you listen to me, you yellow bastard. You're going to pitch the way you used to twenty years ago, Lamburt, when you were the Boy Wonder. Don't tell me you don't have it and you can't do it and all that shit about your arm. You *can* do it and you're *gonna* do it. You're gonna go out there and throw like you used to for the first game and, depending on the situation, for the fifth game too, and you're going to put everything you got into every pitch. *Every* pitch. I don't give a shit about your arm next season or even if you never pitch again.

You're getting paid a million bucks for this season and you damn well better give me my money's worth. 'Cause if you don't, if I even *think* you're dogging it, right after we lose the game, I swear to God I'm going to tear your arm off right there on the field, in front of everybody. On TV. I'll break it at the elbow and then twist it around like a pretzel. And if you think I'm kidding, if you think I can't do it, you can try me right now.'' His face was dark red and the muscles of his arms were twitching as though he barely had them under control. Suddenly he sat down, his face contorted with pain, and pressed his right fist into his belly.

Sullivan, always professional, grabbed Lamburt's left arm hard, and pulled him out of the chair. At the door to the office, he stopped and turned to Bello. "Get your batting gloves and meet me on the field in five minutes. I'll throw you a few easy ones waist-high and you can slam them into the bleachers. Make believe it's Prager's head you're hitting; it'll make you feel better. Otherwise that ulcer'll kill you." He closed the door softly behind him and led Lamburt away from the office. "You see what you done, you stupid bastard? You give Butch a hard time once more with that weak-arm bullshit and I will personally take a bat to your head."

3

The batting-practice pitcher served a fat one to big Isaac Brown, the Jersey Boomers' star left fielder, who promptly hit a low hard drive over the center-field fence 410 feet away. "Goddamn it," Rich Martini yelled to the left-handed pitcher, "put a little more speed on it. You think Carlson or Androvec're going to lob them in to us in the Series? Practice is for *practice*, not for kidding the hitters. And you," he yelled at the broadly smiling Brown, "what the hell are you laughing at? Everybody knows you got the power; what I want you to get is the brains. My little granddaughter could've hit that cripple out too. If I told you once, I told you a thousand times, angle your left foot a little, start that swing a little sooner, and pull it to left. The fence is seventy feet closer in left field."

Brown just smiled widely, turned to the pitcher, planted his feet, and drove the next fastball off the center-field wall. "They'll never learn," Martini grumbled to Dan Zarik. "Once, just once, I'd like to have a hitter who thinks a little bit instead of just swinging."

"As long as he keeps breaking down the walls," Zarik said, "I'm happy. Don't try to change his swing now. Or his timing. I seen plenty of good hitters ruined by too much thinking."

"It don't take thinking to pull the ball a little."

"Brown's a natural. Leave him alone and he'll do what's right when the time comes. Work on Grasso; he's been pressing too hard lately. He's a worrier."

"I'm working on him. I keep telling him he's the greatest natural hitter since Shoeless Joe Jackson. By Saturday, he'll believe it, you'll see, and he'll tear the hide off the ball." He looked closely at the manager. "You sound a little worried, Dan. You know something I don't?"

The old man shook his head. "Nothing like that. I just been thinking myself, that's all." Warmed by the afternoon sun, the two old friends stood at the edge of the grass in front of the home-team dugout in New Jersey's shining new Hague Stadium, the most beautiful ballpark in the majors.

"What's there to think about, Dan? We're the best team in baseball. On top of that, we won the pennant in four straight; the Bandits went a full seven games. They're tired and their pitching is in trouble. Who they gonna start in the first game Saturday? Carlson, with two days' rest, or Androvec, with three? After the way they been sweating the past week? The past month? Nah, they got to start either Padilla or Muldoon. Who haven't been doing too good lately. And they're all lefties to boot, against our three big righties. And Casey can hit lefties pretty good too. We'll win the Series no problem."

"I know, I know, but I want to really rack them up. All the way." The grizzled Zarik stood as straight and tall as when he had been the best center fielder in baseball. "Lucky" they had called him. Somehow, instinctively—he himself didn't know how he did it—he was always standing near where the ball was hit; made every catch look easy. And when he caught the fly ball, he could throw strikes across home plate, so that it took a really fast man to score from third, no matter how deeply the ball had been hit. Zarik was staring at the left-field fence, his pale-blue eyes measuring, visualizing his right-handed power hitters pulling the ball along the left foul line the 340 feet needed to produce another crushing homer. "I want to beat 'em four straight, Richie. Four straight. With big scores." He pulled back his lips in a death's-head smile, the deeply tanned, leathery face wrinkling into a momentary mask of evil. "Real *big* scores."

"You still got it in for Butch Bello?" Martini asked. The dark-complexioned, heavyset batting coach, though ten years younger than his manager, had widened at the hips and thickened at the belly, developments that had been presaged in his last year as an active player when, as a pinch hitter, his booming hits would score even a slow runner from second while he himself, had trouble getting safely to first base. In spite of his brute appearance and his power hitting, Richard Martini was a scientific batter who had cataloged all the pitchers in the league and could spot the hitch in a batter's swing in seconds. "Butch ain't a bad guy, Dan. I played against him myself and I never had any real trouble with him. Except for his mouth."

"Butch has a real big mouth, but it's not Bello I've got it in for," Zarik said. "It's that bastard Prager."

"Yeah, well, *him*." Richie thought for a moment, then added, "That was partly your fault, Dan. You knew what he was like. You shouldn't have taken over the job when he fired Butch. What he did to Butch—you knew for sure he would do it to you, first chance he got."

"I figured I was safe. I had a good lawyer and a tight contract. Figured I was safe for two years, at least."

"Prager got a hundred good lawyers to do nothing but figure out how to screw. Even with a perfect contract, he still had the right to fire you, as long as he paid you. He only took you on to teach Bello a lesson, show him who was boss. He never meant for you to be manager for more than a couple of months."

"I gave up a good team to take that job. When I took over, the Bandits were in sixth place. By the end of the season, we were in second. One more season and I could have had a winner. That's a hell of a payoff, to get fired for doing a good job."

"You got the money."

"Money ain't everything, Rich. I wanted to build a team I could be proud of. I wanted the owner to appreciate what I did, not to tell me, in front of all the reporters, that I stank because I didn't take the team from the bottom to the top in three months."

"Prager wants a screamer, Dan, not a planner. There's no way you could've satisfied him even if you stood on your head. Now do us both a favor and get off that kick. There's no way you can outfigure a moron like that. He'll always find a new way to screw things up nobody ever thought of before. You brought me out here to work out something for the Series; let's work it out."

Dan Zarik was silent for a full minute. He looked his batting coach up and down slowly before he spoke. "How'd you like to change the batting order?" he asked carefully.

"For the Series, you mean? Or for good?"

"Just for the Series. On account of all them lefty pitchers the Bandits got. And to screw up Butch's plans."

"Whaddaya got in mind, Dan? I don't know if I even want to hear it. We got a pretty good combination going. Any kind of change could mess things up, even if it sounds good."

"First give me what you know about Warren Lamburt; he's the key to what I been thinking about."

"You got to understand, all I know is what I hear from our scouts. There's nothing I saw myself, but they all tell me the same thing. Lamburt's arm is gone. Nothing serious, just the old zip ain't there anymore."

"Control? He can still put them where he wants to?"

"He always could and he always will, but slow. He's been fooling around with a knuckler, I hear, but Bello don't let him use it much. Last few games he got hit pretty hard. Real hard. It was only the fielding saved his ass."

"If you was Bello, would you pitch him in the Series?"

"You mean, at all? Hell yes, I would. I ain't a pitching coach, and maybe you should ask Irv Nessen, but I know batting inside out. If I was Bello I'd start Lamburt sometime. There's no way I'd put in all four lefty pitchers in a row, especially against us. Once our guys get zeroed in on hitting lefties, we'll kill them. On top of that, we got four of the best sluggers in the majors, and three of them are righties. I'm just guessing, you understand, but the way I'd do it is start Lamburt in the third game, just to give us something else to

25

look at. I figure Padilla in the first game, Muldoon in the second, then the travel day, then Lamburt, with Carlson and Androvec good and rested for the crucial games. Why you ask?''

"I been wondering how important is having left-handed pitchers against left-handed hitters and right-handed pitchers against right-handed batters. When a pitcher is hot, it don't matter which side the batter swings from. And when a pitcher don't have it, it still don't matter.''

"It's not a sure thing, Dan, but it matters all right. Baseball is fractions of an inch and thousandths of a second. Those tiny little advantages, they don't look like much, but put them all together and they could add up to a win instead of a loss, especially in a tight game. The way I feel about it, I'd sacrifice twenty points in batting average, maybe more, to put a right-handed hitter against a left-handed pitcher. In a short series, that is.''

Zarik nodded. "That's what I figured you'd say; I just wanted to hear you say it out loud now. So you could take the rap along with me, in case it don't work.'' He drew a deep breath and said, slowly, "I want to move our right-handed hitters up the batting order a bit.''

"Change the batting order? What for? It's practically perfect now for against lefties.''

"How'd you like to put Sam Battles on third instead of Conroy?''

"Conroy's got a higher batting average and he's a better fielder.''

"He's just a shade better fielder and he bats lefty. Battles's a righty and his average ain't all that much less than Conroy's. You just said you'd sacrifice twenty points for a righty. Besides, Battles's got good eyes; gets lots of walks.''

"First? You figuring on putting him up first? He's a long-ball hitter.''

"Casey Stengel sometimes put in a slugger to lead off. He figured that a home run right off would take the steam out of the other team.''

"I don't like it, Dan. We got it licked just the way it is. Let's play it conservative. Put a fast man up first, just to get on base, the second guy up to advance him, then let the sluggers go to town. Why take chances?''

26

"There's more, Rich. I want to push Casey down to bat seventh."

Martini's normally ruddy complexion got even redder. "Come on, Dan; he's got the most RBI's on the team. Fifth is the perfect place for him."

"He's a lefty. I want to have the first six men the Bandits face all righties, whether it's Padilla or Muldoon pitching, or even Androvec. I want to get two, three runs the first inning, put the Bandits in the hole from the start. After that, I don't think they can take the pressure; they'll be throwing the ball all over field."

"You mean you're going to play Carter in right field instead of Grasso? You're asking for trouble, Dan. Big trouble. I wouldn't play Carter at all in the Series. That crazy bastard hates the Bandits more than you and, what's worse, he don't have any sense. A pitcher brushes him back, which is legit because he crowds the plate so much, and Carter rushes him with the bat in his hands. Not just fists; with the *bat*. Remember when he swung at Vasco? If they hadn't tackled him, he would have taken the kid's head off."

"Grasso bats left, and you yourself told me he's been a little nervous lately, pressing. Carter's a righty."

"It ain't worth the risk, Dan. Honest, if I could do it, I wouldn't even want Carter on the bench this Series. If there's a fight on the field, and he joined in—and he'd be the first one out of the dugout—he could kill somebody."

"With Carter batting second, that'll give us six righties in a row. By the time they get to our two lefties, both of them good hitters, Padilla will be pressing, throwing scared. We might even get four runs to start off with."

"Only two lefties? You figuring on using Harriman for starting pitcher the first game?"

"With the first two games at the Dome, we can't use a DH. Harriman's our best right-hander, ain't he? That'll give us seven right-handed hitters in the lineup against a lefty pitcher."

"I don't like it, Dan. I figured you were going to start Wade, then go to Farinella or Devine. Wade did real good his last start and he's got the best ERA on the team. I don't mind if the pitcher strikes out, as long as he pitches good. What you're doing, Dan, you're betting everything on the hitting.''

"That's exactly it. Our game is slugging, and if we get a good start, our hitters'll be bouncing 'em off the fences all day long. You know how it is when you got a rally going; even the pitchers hit.''

"I don't know, Dan. Our pitching staff ain't the greatest in the league and the Bandits got some pretty good hitters too. They're going to get some runs off us even if we put in our best pitchers, but we got to keep the numbers down. You put in Harriman and we got problems. You're trying to put us in a slugging match with the Bandits. Yeah, we'll probably beat them, but don't forget, they got four real good pitchers, even if they're all lefties, and we ain't going to get as many runs as you think. I say we use our best pitchers as much as possible—even on a three-day rotation, I don't care in a short series—pull them out the second they get tired and throw in a reliever, and play the game the way we do it the best.''

"No. The way I see it, we beat their brains in the first innings of the first game, we break their spirit, then we walk all over them the other three games. I want to beat them by the biggest scores in the history of the Series.''

"Listen to me, Dan,'' Martini pleaded. "You're letting the way you hate Prager ruin your judgment. I don't care if we win by one run or ten, as long as we win. I want the honor of two World Series in a row and I want the winner's share of the money. As long as we win four, I don't give a damn how we do it, even if the Series goes the full seven games. As long as we win. You're concentrating on the batting. OK, I'm the batting coach, and I know how important hitting is, but pitching is eighty percent of the game. You know that as well as I do, Dan. Better. You sacrifice any one part of the game to another part, and you got trouble. Especially if it's pitching. You got to have balance on a team.''

"I got balance. Harriman is a pretty good pitcher. He may not be up to Wade or Farinella, but he's dependable, steady, and he's also one of the best-hitting pitchers in the league. You also got to consider who you're playing against. The Bandits barely got into the playoffs and they won the pennant by a couple of lucky breaks. On top of that, Prager, the stupid bastard, loaded up the team with four lefty pitchers and, with Lebko out, that leaves only one right-handed starter. Warren Lamburt. Who's lost his speed. There's no way Bello's going to let him start, and we got nothing but lefties to face. So I'm playing the odds just the way you wanted. What's wrong with that?''

"Nothing, Dan. On paper, nothing. But I don't like the idea of concentrating on that one thing only. We got a winning team—let's not change things.''

"We got other things going for us too, Richie. Mainly Prager himself. He's got his heart and soul wrapped up in the Bandits. It's like he put himself on the line; his whole life is bet on the Bandits. In his head, it's his team *personally*. If I crush his team, it's just like I was crushing him. He's been going around, like always, telling the press what a genius he is and what a bum Bello is, praising his million-dollar stars and knocking the rest of the players. What do you think that does for morale?''

"Morale is important, sure, but it ain't everything.''

"With the Bandits it is. What I'm counting on is Sam Prager. What do you think he'll do if we score big in the first inning? He'll be sending messages down to Bello every two minutes, making him change this, change that, do crazy things. He'll drive Bello wild— you know what a temper he's got—and the players'll be so confused that they won't remember what position they're playing. We'll take them in four straight.''

"It'll be just as good if we beat them four out of seven, like we're sure to do if we just play our regular ball game. You turn things upside down, bet everything on the slugging, and who knows what's going to happen.''

"I don't want it just as good. I want to slaughter Prager, really show him up for the bum he is. Besides, I'm not just going to concentrate on the hitting. We're going to play a more aggressive game on the field too, keep up the pressure all the time. Take long leads off the bases, put the pitchers and catchers on edge. Run out every hit full speed, even sure outs. Make them throw the ball away. On double plays, knock the second baseman down hard. Spikes high, like Ty Cobb. Everything. Aggressive all the way, Pete Rose–style.''

''So that's why you put Carter in, isn't it?'' Rich Martini stared at his manager. ''You're not just looking to bury them, Dan; you're looking to kill them first.''

''Now you got the idea, Rich.'' Zarik nodded grimly. ''Make sure the players understand it.''

Martini shook his head. ''I don't like it, Dan. What you got against Prager—you're taking it out on his team.''

Zarik glared at his batting coach. ''You got a better way?'' There was no answer. ''Then make sure you do what I told you, how I told you.''

4

Samuel Moultran Prager, with a busty young blonde on his arm, walked into the Brooklyn Bandits' public-relations meeting room as regally as a short, skinny, middle-aged playboy could. Parking the beautiful young woman on a corner chair in the front of the room, from which she could watch his masterful handling of the news media—and the media could watch this evidence of his good taste and manly popularity—he approached the end of the podium and waited impatiently for his PR people to spring to his presence. Though he held himself stiffly erect, as ordered by his tailor, the skillfully cut Italian suit of soft tan cashmere did not quite hide his little pot belly, nor did the carefully arranged dyed-blond hair quite cover his sunburned scalp. The blue-irised contact lenses gave Prager's eyes a slightly froggish look as he made a practiced count of the reporters and noted the number of empty chairs. The wrinkles twitched into sharp creases around his thin smile as he turned to George Blondin, the VP in charge of PR and whispered, "Where are the rest of them?"

"Joe DiMaggio just came into town," Blondin apologized, "and half of them went to interview him."

"I'm paying you a lot more than you're worth to do a very simple job, Georgie," Prager said, just loudly enough to be heard by everybody in the room. "Next time I call a press conference, there better be a full house. Or else. And fix the microphone to the proper height *before* I get up there. In fact, I want that mike stand screwed to the right height all the time; everybody else can use a hand-held. Got it?''

Blondin flushed and, head carefully averted from the crowd of reporters, climbed the two steps up to the platform. He moved the microphone down almost a foot—Prager liked to have tall men around him—and bent over as inconspicuously as he could. ''Ladies and gentlemen of the press,'' he said, smiling weakly, ''Mr. Prager has an important message for you. There will be a question period after his announcement and you will still have plenty of time to phone in your story or to make the six o'clock news. Now, I give you Mr. Sam Prager, owner of the National League Champion Brooklyn Bandits.'' He clapped his hands enthusiastically. There were exactly two short, scornful claps from the audience.

Prager mounted the podium, walked briskly to the microphone, and smiled all around the big room. At a signal from Blondin, the room lights were lowered and a spot was focused on Prager, making his absolutely perfect teeth sparkle. ''Good afternoon, ladies and gentlemen of the media,'' Prager said. ''I want to welcome you to the home of the new National League Champions and the soon-to-be new World Champions, the Brooklyn Bandits.'' There were derisive snickers throughout the room at this. Prager looked carefully, but with the darkened room and the spotlight in his eyes, he couldn't make out the culprits. ''I want you to know it hasn't been easy. I spent a lot of time and money planning this, a hell of a lot of money, and I had a lot of opposition and bitching, some of it even from inside the organization, but in the end, I won. Though, actually, I had it figured to come in four years. Sometimes, no matter how careful you are, things don't get done the way they should. Not everybody has got the drive and the will, the stick-to-it quality, that moves mountains.''

''I thought it took faith to move mountains,'' one reporter yelled.

''That too.'' Prager took it in stride. ''I had enough faith to spend what I had to to get the best. The *very* best. And when it became available, I got it. I wanted the greatest outfield in baseball, and I got it. Demarco, Rigdale, Wilder, and Coffee. Is there a better outfield than that?''

"Only three of them can play at a time," another voice yelled.

"Depth is what we've got," Prager responded. "And did it ever occur to you wise guys that if I got an extra star outfielder, the opposition doesn't have him? Think about that for a while. And the same with my pitching staff: four of the best there is. Plus Warren Lamburt, who is going to pitch for me like he did five years ago."

"Did you buy him a new arm too?" a third voice asked.

"I've been saving him for just this occasion. The minute he looked like he got a little tired, I sent a message to Butch Bello to relieve him. Lamburt's a valuable property; can't have him straining his arm. I've been attending every game this past month, which is why we put on that terrific last-minute drive that brought us the pennant. I only wish that I could have taken the time—I got a lot of business interests, you know, that demand my personal attention— to be with my team from the beginning of the season on so we could have tied up the pennant a month earlier. But I'm only one man. . . ." He turned up his hands helplessly. "Anyway, during the whole World Series I'm going to be talking to Butch Bello from my box whenever I see something that needs doing and we're going to win the Series. That I guarantee. Now, any questions?"

Marc Burr jumped up first. "Mr. Prager, how can you *guarantee* that the Bandits will win the Series? You might have heard that the Boomers are a pretty good team too. If I bet on the Bandits, based on your guarantee, will you refund my money if I lose my bet?"

Prager turned red. "You know what I mean. I got a great team that—they know how generous I can be if they make me happy. The World Series winner's shares won't be a hill of beans compared to the bonuses they'll get if they produce what I know they're capable of. They got an incentive to win, a real *good* incentive."

"What happens if they lose?" another reporter asked.

"There's going to be a lot of new minor leaguers around if they don't win like I know they can. If I pay for the best, I better get the best action."

"What about the ones with the long-term contracts?"

"They can be traded to teams that will never get out of second division, even if I got to foot the bill. What's the point in having stars if they don't play like stars?''

"Does that go for Butch Bello too? Isn't his contract up this year?''

"Butch Bello is my type of guy—I love him, a real aggressive manager who doesn't take any crap from the opposition. Or the umpires, either. He knows I'm ready to extend his contract for another year when we win the Series.''

"Only another year? For doing a great job?''

"He does another great job, he's got another year. There's not going to be any more long-term contracts on the Bandits anymore. And don't forget, I was the one who told him, every day, what to do the past month. It wasn't just Butch.''

"What if the Bandits don't win?''

"The only way we won't win is if Bello disregards my suggestions. He's too smart to do that.''

"You'll fire him if he doesn't do what you tell him? Then what do you need a manager for?''

"There are lots of routine situations which Butch is perfectly capable of handling himself, and lots of administrative situations which no owner wants to bother with. The only time I give Bello advice is when I see something he's missed—because he's concentrating on one aspect of the game, you see—that I can see more clearly, so I just remind him of what's the right thing to do at that time.'' Prager glanced at George Blondin.

Immediately, Blondin went up to the microphone, bent down, and said, "Thank you, Mr. Prager." Blondin applauded. No one took up the cue. "For those of you who want personal interviews, close up, for your six o'clock shows, Mr. Prager will now come down to the floor and give you all the quotes you need, individually. Just remember to keep it short; there are others waiting too. For whoever's finished, the phones are available in the back room, where there are the usual refreshments laid on.''

Blondin escorted Prager down to the floor in front of the platform. Marc pulled the PR man aside. "You used to be a good announcer, George, and a star player; how can you stand that shit?''

"I have a family now, Marc," Blondin said ruefully. "For them I can take anything. If you ever . . . You'll find out what I mean someday."

In the shadow of the far doorway Butch Bello clutched his belly and said to Verne Sullivan, "Some day I'm going to kill that bastard, Verne. I'm really going to kill him."

"When the time comes," Sullivan said, "let me know. I'll help."

5

"You're home early," Dahliah Norman said as Marc pulled shut the freight elevator's big steel door, the only easy entrance to their illegal top-floor loft. He carefully locked the heavy dead bolt before he turned around. No matter how many times he saw her like this, even after a year together, Dahliah still looked lovely in his eyes, a thing of beauty and a joy forever. She was standing in their kitchen, a room delineated only by the partial enclosure formed by freestanding kitchen cabinets. Dahliah had put on a loose yellow housedress, shucking her formal professor's gray tweed suit along with her staid demeanor as soon as she entered their home. Barefoot, she was now no taller than Marc. He stopped for a moment just to look at her, to enjoy the sight of her long auburn hair and green eyes, her Devonshire-cream skin and her full-curved figure. He remembered what George Blondin had told him, how for his family he would take anything from Slippery Sam Prager, and Marc felt a shock of understanding. For Dahliah, there was nothing he would not do. Nothing. Even if she never married him. Foolish thought, really. Pointless. He wasn't getting any younger and, for that matter, neither was Dahliah, so her wanting to wait seemed as senseless as it was frustrating. "I'll be home even earlier tomorrow," Marc said. "The Boomers will be practicing at the Gruber Dome and I won't have to go over to Jersey to get a story on them."

"If it's that close, do you want to take your good camera?"

"When I'm working, I don't think of art. For emergencies, my little auto-focus will be enough to carry." He let out his breath wearily.

"Anything bad happen?" Dahliah looked at him anxiously. "Witter after you again?"

"He's always after me. The trouble is, I don't know if he means it or if it's his own nasty way of trying to train me. Like a dancing bear. After fifteen years in the job, he's still using the whip to drive me the way he wants me to go, to become just like him."

"You could never be just like him, darling, and I wouldn't want you to change in any way. Except maybe to worry less. You look very tense. Go do some exercise for a while. Take a slow hot shower too. Supper isn't ready; I didn't expect you till later."

Marc dropped his portable computer terminal on the bed in their sleeping area—only the bathroom was fully enclosed—and walked to the front half of the huge, high-ceilinged loft, a complete gymnastic practice area, its walls covered with the big color photographs of gymnasts in action that Marc had taken during the '72 Olympics, when he had been the only American to place in the top twenty scorers. He stripped quickly, put on his work-out clothes, and went into his routine of stretching and loosening exercises, concluding by hanging from the horizontal bar, relaxing his body completely, trying to clear his head of all problems, allowing gravity to pull him into a long, straight, still line. After a full minute, after he felt the tension drain from his muscles and his mind, he kipped up and began a series of drop kips, ending with two giant swings and a simple backflip dismount.

He lay down, supine, on the mat that covered the whole front half of the loft, breathing in fast and deeply, and exhaling very, very slowly, until his pulse rate dropped and he felt the small of his back approach the mat. Rolling his legs back over his head, he kipped up and did a series of forward dives and rolls until he reached the side horse. He grabbed the pommel, pressed up, made a few swings, and began practicing a windmill, clumsily and with less-than-acceptable extension—at thirty-seven, gymnasts and dogs do not learn new tricks easily—then dismounted neatly. He chained a pair of backflips, building up speed, another flip with a half-twist, and finished with a double forward to reach the parallel bars, where, without a stop, he mounted and did a simple routine of rolls and stands, a one-hand stand, a drop to a lever, a two-hand planche—in which his body was much too far from the horizontal—and a backflip dismount.

Breathing heavily and sweating hard, he lay down on the mat again and began a series of relaxation exercises, lifting portions of his body slightly, then lowering them and continuing the feeling of lowering even after he touched the mat. After several minutes he felt loose again and fully warmed up. He ran to the still rings, jumped, caught the rings, and kipped up into a straight handstand, went around three times in pike position, then into an almost-good crucifix with legs extended. He held the position for a full five seconds, until he felt his abdominal muscles and shoulders screaming, swung twice to get height—the ceiling wasn't quite high enough for full maneuvering—then dismounted with a front flip. Without stopping his forward motion, he hurried to the bathroom, dropping his clothes on the way, and turned on a warm shower.

He switched the showerhead to a hard, pulsing massage and, eyes closed, slowly turned until every portion of his glowing body relaxed. Gradually he turned down the hot water until the shower was slightly cool, shut it off and toweled himself roughly. He put on his white terry-cloth bathrobe and went to the kitchen, to Dahliah.

"I splurged today," she confessed. "They had some beautiful huge *porcini,* just flown in from Italy. Twelve dollars a pound, but it's been so long since we had some really great mushrooms. . . . I got a semolina bread too, and some expensive virgin olive oil."

"Can't you understand," Marc asked, "that we can afford to splurge like this once in a while? After the raises I squeezed out of Witter in the Super Bowl murder story, we can even afford to eat out every week."

"I know, but with all the money we spent on putting in central heating and the money I'm trying to save to buy a loft of our own . . . If the city ever inspects this building, they'll made us move out because we're not an industry."

"I can always tell them we're running a gym."

"And if they ask for a list of your students? Or to see the books? Or the tax receipts?"

"Why can't your karate class meet here? We'll charge them a low rent, and that'll help the budget too."

"Have everybody poking around the apartment? Where we don't even have doors to close? And using my bathroom? This is my home, Marc, our home."

"OK, OK. What's the chances of your getting a raise?"

"A small raise? Very good. But my raises will come very slowly; there's nothing I can do about that. You're our only hope."

"I'm about as high as I can go in sports. My only chance is that Witter will let me shift to straight news, become an investigative reporter. Political reporting—that's where the real opportunities are. Uncover one major scandal and your fortune's made. Books, movies, TV . . ."

"Witter will never let you go, you know that. In spite of the way he treats you, he knows you're his best reporter and he needs you. Why don't you threaten to go to another paper?"

"The other papers are stuffed full with sports reporters and columnists, all top people. They're not going to fire one of them to make room for me. The only change he'll allow will be for me to work on 'The Sporting Woman' page. Under the thumb of Nelda Shaver."

"And other parts of her anatomy?" Dahliah's teeth clenched. "That's one change *I* won't allow."

"Relax, Dahliah, I'll never do it. Especially if we're married."

"Especially? What does that mean?"

"I didn't mean it that way. All I meant was—marriage vows, things like that. Strengthen the bonds. Until death do us part. I'm ready anytime you are."

"I told you last week, I'm thinking about it."

"Well?"

"I'm still thinking."

Marc sighed. "All right, I'll try to be nice to Witter."

"You'll never be able to do that. You and he—"

"All right. How about *nicer?*"

"It won't help. I'm a psychologist, and I know. I see this as a classic father-son conflict, displacement of the father by the son. To Julius Witter, that has to be a fate worse than death."

"Speaking of a fate worse than death, I'm all warmed up and my muscles are almost perfectly relaxed. All I need now is one more little exercise." Marc moved closer to her.

Dahliah twisted away slightly. "You should have thought of that sooner. I've already started sautéing the *porcini;* they'll be ready in a minute and even you aren't that fast. At twelve dollars a pound—"

"You're more interested in money than in love."

"I have to be; I'm a teacher. Sit down now, or else I won't split the dish evenly. And if you're good, maybe after you stuff yourself—"

"Take advantage of the offer while it's hot. After I stuff myself, I may not be in the mood."

"For that you get nothing. Ever. A gallant lover would have given up *two* pounds of *porcini* for me."

Dahliah put one mushroom onto Marc's plate and swept the rest onto her own. "You want to try for stale bread and water tomorrow? *White* bread?"

"The ultimate punishment? Oh for the days when women had 'headaches.' "

"Are you crazy? Why should I deprive myself when you act stupidly?"

"If I don't get a balanced diet," Marc pointed out, "with all the essential amino acids in the proper quantities, you'll be punishing yourself tonight as well as me."

Dahliah immediately pushed half the mushrooms onto Marc's plate. "Logic works," she said, "but poetry works better. Try it someday."

6

The Jersey Boomers were practicing on the unfamiliar artificial turf of the Gruber Dome, getting used to the feel of the faster surface and the unevenness of the artificial lighting. They held back at first, to avoid the sprains and the stubbed toes that were all too common on the less giving surface but, as the morning progressed, shifted gradually into their normal graceful movements, running with accustomed speed, batting and throwing accurately and confidently.

Butch Bello and his entire coaching staff, dressed in their baseball uniforms, were sitting in the glassed-in owner's box, watching the practice and taking notes. "Feels funny sitting in Prager's palace," Verne Sullivan said. "This is some fancy place. You sure it's OK for us to be here?"

"It's OK for me to be here," Bello said. "I called him last night—didn't want to interfere in case he was planning to bring one of his bimbos up here to impress her. He gave me a key to his private box long ago, when he liked me. But he doesn't know I brought all of you here. If he did, he'd have the upholstery cleaned."

"Suppose he drops in unexpectedly?"

"Nah, he never watches practices—afraid he might learn something. Screw him. If he finds out, I'll explain it to him in words of one syllable. Meanwhile, keep your eyes on the field; this is the best place to see everything from, and Dan Zarik can't tell we're watching."

"You think he doesn't know?"

" 'Course he knows, but let him wonder where the hell we are. Give him something else to worry about."

Near the group of coaches were the scouts, pointing out the mannerisms and habits of each of the Boomers' players.

"There's Isaac Brown coming up for batting practice," Earl Diggins, the fat batting coach, said. "He hits dead center, especially on fastballs, and with power, lots of power. When he comes up, the outfielders got to pull back, almost to the track, and bunch in the middle. He hardly ever pulls to left, and almost never hits to right field."

"The way to pitch him," Verne Sullivan said, "is for right-handers to go low, with sinkers and hard curveballs inside—nothing right over the plate. Left-handers should use hard stuff in at the hands, fastballs and sliders. You give him anything straight to hit at and it's good-bye ball game."

"What about a change-up?" Bello asked.

"It better be a straight change, no slower than that. He's got such fast reactions, you give him time to see what's coming and you've had it. A change-up on the first pitch might get him, though."

"Is that Carter in right instead of Grasso?" Bello asked. "What the hell's going on? Is Grasso injured?"

"He was OK yesterday," one of the scouts said. "It gotta be just for practice, just in case. Grasso's been pressing lately, not making full contact with the ball."

"I don't like it," Bello muttered. "Brown and Cordray don't have anybody in for them, why for Grasso? You think Zarik's going to be stupid enough to pull Grasso and start Carter?"

"It might not be a bad move," Sullivan said, with a hard look at Bello. "Get another right-handed batter in against our lefty pitchers.

"Yeah, but to start that maniac against us . . . ? Zarik must've gone crazy."

"Don't worry, Butch," Sullivan said. "If Carter comes into the game, I'll signal the pitcher to put a fast one a foot behind his head."

"You're as bad as he is," Diggins said. "When he ducks into it, he'll be killed."

"Only kidding, Dig. Relax. You worry more about the opposition batters than about your own team." Sullivan veered off. "What're Casey's weaknesses? How do we pitch to him?"

"I got the perfect way to stop him: an intentional base on balls." Diggins smiled ruefully. "Let me ask you something, Verne. Who're they gonna pitch tomorrow?"

"Gotta be Wade or Farinella. Or Devine. If I was the manager, I'd start with Wade; he's been hot lately."

"Well, that narrows it down a lot; it'll be either a right-hander or a left-hander. For a moment there, I was afraid it was going to be a switch-pitcher."

"You keep giving me advice like to walk Casey, and you're lucky if I tell you the time of day."

Marc approached Dan Zarik warily. There was always a frown on Zarik's weathered face, so it was hard to tell if he would bite Marc's head off or give him a good interview "Is it OK if I talk to you now, Dan?"

"We'll be off the field in twenty minutes."

"There'll be a million guys around you then. I'd like to give the Boomers a good buildup, if I can get some exclusive inside dope from you."

"We don't need good buildups." Dan's eyes were watching the action on the field intently. "But if you was to give me Bello's lineup for the first game, I might see my way clear to giving you some inside dope."

"I don't think Butch knows the lineup himself yet, but if he ever gives it to me, I'll be sure to give you a copy of *The Sentry* edition that features it on the front page. Free. Meanwhile, what've you got for me? Or do I have to make up a story that the Boomers are so confident they'll take the Series in four games from the bush Bandits, that they've already made plane reservations home for the fifth day?"

"It don't matter what I tell you, Burr, you're going to make up what I said anyway, just like all the other vultures, so what the hell. Only we got to talk here on the field, and you got to follow me around, wherever I got to go. I got things to keep an eye on." He started walking to home plate, where Rich Martini was hitting fungoes to two outfielders. They, in turn, were whipping in one-bounce throws to Randy Norden, the third-string catcher. "Bounce a few off the walls," Zarik told Martini. "I want them to get the feel of the angles of the rebounds." Martini nodded as Dan passed on to the first base line, Marc following.

"Kidding aside, Dan," Marc pressed, "how do you see the series? For publication."

"Come on, Burr, you know what I got to say for publication. The Bandits are a terrific team and it's gonna be a real hard battle, but I'm confident we'll win. Maybe if we're lucky, we'll do it in six, but I'll be just as happy if it takes seven games, so long as we win."

"I don't need you for that, Dan; I can write that kind of crap myself without leaving the office. You know that the Bandits were lucky. If they hadn't gotten all the breaks, they wouldn't be in the Series. As it is, it took them to the last day to clinch the pennant, and they had the benefit of playing the worst teams in the league the last month, while the other three good teams were beating each other's brains out. The Bandits actually backed into the pennant."

Dan Zarik took his eyes off the field and stared down at Marc. "Sonny, I been in baseball longer than you been on earth, so let me tell you something. Nobody gets to be league champs by accident. Sure, sometimes you get a lucky break, but that evens out, because other times the breaks go the other way. All this talk about our winning in a walk—it's a crock of shit. Anything can happen in a short series. Anything. The difference between one good team and another is a lot of little things adding up, which can be blown away by overconfidence, a bad bounce, a lot of things. The way you guys write us up, if we win, well that's to be expected, no big deal. And if we lose, with the team we got, it gotta be because I'm no good, the manager screwed up. So you better tell your readers that this

Series, any short series, is no pushover, that I got to use every trick in the book to make sure that we win."

"You've got the better team, Dan. You have to admit that."

"Yeah, on paper, I admit it. But you got to realize that the Bandits got a good team too. They got four good outfielders. I know, I know—everybody makes a joke out of it, four star outfielders, but if one gets hurt, or sick, they still got a real good outfield. If Grasso, Brown, or Cordray twists his ankle on this damn plastic turf, or goes blind looking into those lights, I got a much weaker outfield left. When Sam Prager spends, he buys the best, and it's finally paid off for him. These days, forget about developing players, forget about just liking to play ball. It's the guys with the money who ruined the game."

"Does that go for your owners too?"

"Hell, no. They're businessmen, out to make a profit. Can't fault them for that. No way would they spend that kind of money for a pennant: you'd have to win five Series in a row just to break even. Prager's just plain crazy, that's all. Trying to prove something, I guess. What for, I don't know."

"I noticed you had Carter in right field before. Does that mean you're going to start him? Is there anything wrong with Grasso?"

"Not a damn thing's wrong with Grasso; I was just giving an example. If you looked later, you'da seen all my outfielders taking practice."

"Does that mean you're not going to let Carter play in the Series at all? Given his well-known attitude toward the Bandits?"

"It doesn't mean that at all. If it was bases loaded in the last of the ninth, with two out, I'd put in Carter as pinch hitter, even for Casey. Carter—hell, he'd give his life to get the hit that beat the Bandits. Sometimes a manager got to figure personality, desire, aggressiveness, over batting averages."

"Are you claiming the Bandits are a better team than you?"

"Hell no. What I'm saying is that they're not as bad compared to us as the papers've been making out. Take their pitching staff, for instance. They got four starters just as good as Wade. Four. I got two good ones—don't print that; I don't want a hassle in the locker room—Wade and Farinella, and then I pray for rain."

"Those four Bandits pitchers are all lefties."

"Gee, Burr, I never thought of that. You tell poor old suffering Sam Prager that I'll trade him any one of my righties, including Harriman, for any one of those lefties, his choice. Right now, if the Commissioner will allow it."

"They're weak down the middle. Whether Bello puts in Cubby Banneker or Pancho Rivera at short, he's still got problems."

"Yeah, granted, but Joe Kullman and Alvin Smootra can cover the hole pretty good. And with Rivera in there—maybe he can't hit so good, but with him, they got the greatest fielding combo in the majors. And my infield is not the greatest either. If this Series was going to be decided by infield errors, I wouldn't know which way it would go. And don't forget, for the first two games—which can set the attitude, the spirit of the whole Series—they're going to be played in the Gruber Dome, indoors on artificial turf. We haven't played a single game on turf in the past month, while the Bandits played half their games in here."

"You've got today to practice in here and before the game tomorrow."

"Not the same as being used to the field. The home-team advantage—you can't put numbers on it, but it sure makes a difference, a hell of a difference. And with those crazy Brooklyn fans . . .? Maniacs. How'd you like to be a pitcher with three-and-two on the batter and the tying run on base, and thirty thousand maniacs screaming at you to balk? Or a batter, in the same position, trying to concentrate on a ball coming at ninety miles an hour?"

"Granted, home-team advantage counts for something, but you still have the best-slugging team in the majors."

"Yeah, that I do. That's what I'm depending on. We don't have their pitching staff, and we're about equal in fielding, and we may not even get more hits than them, but when we do, we'll outslug them for sure. We'll score more runs with the same number of hits, and that'll be the story."

"That'll be my story too, Dan, but you have one more advantage you haven't mentioned. You run your team."

"Yeah, that's important. You have no idea what it's like living with that bastard Prager. I don't see how Butch can stand it."

"We all felt bad for you when it happened, Dan. Prager really gave you a screwing."

"You have no idea how bad. The promises he made, *swore*, the . . . Ah, what's the use. On the field—that's where I'll show him up for the dumb sonofabitch he is. When he starts passing messages down to Butch—that's when we'll score the most."

"You really hate him, don't you? The Series is going to be a real grudge match."

"Yeah, well, it's not against the Bandits—they're playing ball for a living just like the rest of us. Or against Butch Bello. But it'll give me great satisfaction to win real big. Show Slippery Sam that, with all his money, he's pretty damn poor in the brains department. That man got no class, no class at all—you can print this—and his word ain't worth shit. In fact, he's a piss-poor excuse for a man. Baseball would be a much better place without him. And you can quote me on that too."

"Thanks, Dan, that'll make a good story."

"Not in your column?"

"No, sorry, I can't criticize Prager too much in my column—unofficial policy. But I can quote you in a news story, if you don't mind taking the heat."

"Hell, no—what can he do to me that he ain't already done? But you want good quotes on Prager, you gotta talk to Butch Bello. He's been taking that shit on and off for five years, and one of these days his ulcer's going to pop. I got a feeling he's ready to tell off Prager right at the end of the Series. I'd like to be there when that happens, watch Sam's face. It'd make up for some of what he did to me."

"I'd like to be there too, but I probably won't be invited. I'm going to talk to Butch later; can I quote you to him? And to Prager? It'll make a real good story."

"Not on Butch; I really got nothing against him. But on Prager?

47

Anything I say about him, you can quote me in spades. If I'm lucky—hell, if we're all lucky—maybe he'll get a stroke when he reads it.''

Earl Diggins looked at his watch. "It's almost twelve, Butch, and I haven't eaten since breakfast. The Boomers are just about finished anyway, nothing more to see. What do you say we break for lunch?''

"Yeah, OK," Bello said. "There's coffee and doughnuts, Danish, fruit, and plenty of juices and soft drinks laid out in the locker room.''

"Let's get down there fast," Diggins said. "I don't want the players eating too much before practice.''

"Don't worry, Earl, there'll be plenty left for you," Bello said.

"Plenty?" Diggins said over his shoulder, halfway out the door. "That's my favorite.''

"Use the stairs going down, too, not any elevator; the less people know about all of us being up here, the less chance I got to fight with Prager about that in addition.''

"You're not going to eat any doughnuts, are you, Butch?" Verne Sullivan was solicitous. "They're fried.''

"Can't now," Bello answered. "The ulcer's been acting up. If I even go near the stuff, just smell it . . . I'll get a couple of yogurts from my office refrigerator. Pick up your sandwiches and coffee and meet me in the dugout. I want to talk to you private before the other guys come out.''

"What's on your mind? I'll think about it meanwhile.''

"Relievers. We can't use them all up in one game. How long we gonna keep Lamburt in after they start hitting him?''

There were some players from both teams throwing balls around the field, but nothing worth watching. Marc was standing near the home-team dugout, watching for Bello. He saw the burly manager coming out of his tunnel and walked along the first base line to meet him halfway. "How about an interview, Butch?" Marc asked.

"I'm busy now," Butch said, not slowing down. He was carrying a thin plastic bag; Marc could see a banana and two containers of yogurt. "Later."

"Witter wants an exclusive personal interview or else he's going to send me to City Hall and put Nelda Shaver on the Bandits. You want her in your locker room?"

Bello made a disgusted face. "You trying to blackmail me? OK, Burr, but not now. I'll see you right after practice. In my office, four o'clock."

"You know you won't be there on time. You'll be talking to the coaches after practice. I don't want to hang around in the dark outside your office until you're finished. Why'd you pick the furthest tunnel anyway?"

"To make me hard to find. Nobody ever comes to see me with good news, and if I'm near the locker room, anytime one of my millionaires gets his teeny-weeny feelings hurt, he comes in and gives me a sob story. This way, he gets a little exercise if he wants to find me. That goes for reporters too. You guys ain't been too cooperative lately."

"You want a good story, Butch, be nice to me."

"OK, you got my permission to go in my waiting room. It's unlocked and there's magazines there. Meanwhile, stay off the field. You want to interview any of the players, wait till they finish practice."

"Can I go in the bullpen? Interview Carlson?"

"OK, go in the bullpen, but leave Carlson alone—he's nervous enough already."

"Does that mean you're going to start Carlson? With only two days' rest?"

"That don't mean nothing. You want to interview somebody, go talk to Lamburt. He'll give you ten columns' worth on how he's going to beat the Boomers with nothing but knuckleballs."

"Now I know you're lying, Butch. You haven't let Lamburt throw a single knuckler all year."

"He snuck in a few; I don't always lie to reporters. Like when I was a catcher, calling the signals. Sometimes I throw in a little bit of truth, just to keep you off-balance.''

''And then you scream I misquoted you.''

''Sure, Burr, same as you reporters do. It's part of the game. If you guys had the balls to print the truth, the real truth, maybe we'd all tell you the whole story.'' He looked angry and, for a moment, Marc was afraid the manager would take out on him the troubles, the harassment, he'd suffered the past five years. But Bello took a deep breath, then another, and calmed down. ''Now I got to go to work.'' he said quietly. ''See you at four. Maybe five after. You be on time; I'll try to be there on time too.''

7

Marc watched the practice for a while, noting that, unlike the high-spirited, confident Boomers, the Bandits were dragging, looking tired and depressed, as though they had already lost the Series. A team in that frame of mind would lose, would defeat themselves, and that would have to be the thrust of his column this afternoon. He knew it would affect the judgment of the last-minute bettors, but it was his function to present the news and, in the column, his views, regardless of their effect. The odds on the Boomers winning in seven games were hovering around 9–5, a rather high ratio for a short series, and his column might raise that to 2–1. But it couldn't be helped. The odds-makers, the local bookies, knew at least as much as he did, if not more—after all, unlike reporters, they had to put their money where their mouths were—and they were certainly going to keep the odds on the favorite sufficiently high so the Brooklyn fans would be encouraged to bet against what seemed to be a sure thing.

The other *Sentry* reporters would be interviewing the individual players, writing up the comparative statistics, doing the routine things that had to be done to fill the sports pages. As a bylined sports reporter and a three-times-a-week sports columnist, Marc had to concentrate on the unusual and the intimate. With lots of time to kill before he could interview Butch Bello, he took the elevator to the upstairs press room to write the Boomers story and the column describing the visible differences between the attitudes of the two

51

teams. The story flowed and, Marc thought, the column even sparkled a bit. Practice, practice, practice, that's what does it. And maybe even a bit of Julius Witter's constant harping on smooth, concise, accurate, informative writing had rubbed off. Witter might be a mean bastard, but he was also a smart bastard. After a single rewrite, Marc plugged his modem into the telephone and had his portable computer terminal send in both the story and the column to *The Sentry*'s computer.

Marc decided to go downstairs, to wander about the labyrinth of corridors under the stands, and to see what color stories he could pick up for future use or as sidebars attached to other stories. Just as he got out of the elevator, on a sudden whim, he turned right and walked along the wide main corridor to the home team's training area.

Tall, skinny Popeye was there, old Jake Pitney, refilling the partly empty shelves and the glass-doored cabinets with rolls of tape of various widths, liniments, antiseptics, standard medications, and mysterious unlabeled bottles and plastic containers, checking off the items on his clipboard, preparing for the Series.

"Just the man I wanted to see," Popeye said, putting down the clipboard. There was nothing wrong with his sharp blue eyes, but his forearms were so big, especially in comparison with his thin upper arms, that "Popeye" was the only name anyone had ever called him. "This gymnastic stuff they built in for the Wizards. I talked to Pusher Rybek and he told me how great it was. I know you don't have three-hundred-pound gorillas twirling by one pinky, so how do you use it? Should I ask the boss to put that kind of apparatus in for us next year? Now that we won the pennant, maybe he'll be in a good mood."

"It'll be better if I show you," Marc offered. "It's right next to Rybek's office."

They set off through the dimly lit central corridor, their footsteps echoing from the bare concrete walls, passing the three-foot-deep recesses with their color-coded doors that indicated the offices, the team areas, and the storage rooms. If anybody thinks I've got a desk job, Marc thought, they don't know how much running around I get to do during a normal workday. "If Rybek would let me use his office," Popeye Pitney complained, "it'd make life a lot more easier for me."

"You're just as fussy as he is," Marc said, "so don't complain." They had to pass through the home-team trainer's area, with its rows of large and small whirlpool baths, the massage cubicles, and the diathermy machines, to get to the single entrance to the gymnasium. The big, high-ceilinged room was overcrowded, with the mats and the standard gymnastic apparatus fitted in between the rows of strength-building Nautilus and Universal machines, and the racks of barbells and dumbbells. "I been in here lots of times," Popeye told Marc, "but this is set up for football. In baseball, we can't use so much weight. You build up a guy too much, and he can't hit or throw or run as good."

"Football players need the bulk and the strength," Marc said, "and they're still pretty fast. But you're right—most of what they have here is not suitable for baseball players. That goes for the gymnastic apparatus too. You can use some of what's here for the Bandits, but if Prager gives you another room, I think the most important thing should be a big mat, a tumbling mat, at least thirty by thirty, and even bigger if you can get it in. The way most infielders dive for a ball, they should have lots of practice learning how to tuck under as they land, to prevent sprains. Outfielders too. These days they throw themselves after a ball the way only infielders used to."

"OK, if I could get somebody to teach them. You wanna?"

"Can't. Conflict of interest, even if I had the time. There are plenty of ex-gymnasts around; get one of them."

"What about the equipment? Which can I use?"

"Don't even look at the side horse or the parallel bars. Baseball players are mostly too heavy to do any kind of gymnastics well, and most of them are in lousy physical condition compared to other athletes. Baseball players depend on their eye-hand skills, the fast response times, their neuromuscular coordination."

"No gymnastic stuff at all?"

"A pair of still rings or a trapeze is useful to hang from and to drop from. Some outfielders jump awfully high against the fence going after a potential homer; practice in landing from a height is essential. But don't let them try any fancy tricks—just hanging and dropping, maybe a slight swing. Also don't let them jump to grab the ring—that's a good way to pull a shoulder muscle—make them use stands to get up. I think the most important piece of apparatus for them is the horizontal bar, but it should be used just for hanging."

"That's all?"

"It's enough. Hanging, if it's done properly, loosens you up mentally as well as physically. Watch." Marc put down his portable computer terminal, jumped up, and caught the bar. "Most people, the first time, hold themselves tightly together," Marc said, "like this. A big strain, and very tiring. Now watch." He closed his eyes, let his head fall back, and relaxed. His body visibly stretched several inches and, as Popeye watched, slowly grew even longer. Marc hung for a full minute, then kipped up and performed two giant swings and a simple backflip dismount. "Don't even let them try that part. I was just showing off."

"Yeah, pretty good for a guy your age." Popeye looked properly impressed. "I didn't know you still worked out. Thanks, Marc. I'll talk to Prager, see if I can get the mat and a big room for tumbling. See how it works next year."

"Glad to be of help," Marc said sincerely, "but you owe me a story."

"You news guys are all alike. OK, the Bandits are in pretty good condition and, 'less one gets hit by a car, they'll all be in top form for the game tomorrow."

"Come on, Popeye, a real story. You're in the best position of anybody to know what's going on, stuff that even Butch Bello doesn't know. Betting? Throwing games? Illegal substances applied to the balls or the bats? Drugs?"

"We don't have any spitballers on the team, but I won't swear

54

the catchers don't scuff up the ball a little, same as any other team. Other than that, nothing. Least nothing I would talk about to a reporter. Betting? I'm sure some ballplayers on all the teams bet once in a while, but nothing I know of direct. What for? These days, even the rookies get as much as Babe Ruth used to get in his prime, so why mess around? Nobody throws games either. Nobody. That's crazy. In baseball, only the pitcher can really throw a game, or a pinch hitter, and if he does, it's gonna cost him more than he could ever make from betting. Drugs? I hear plenty of rumors, but I can tell you straight, if anybody on the Bandits is hooked, I don't know about it. Far as other things go, smoking I mean, I don't see any big signs of that either, so it got to be casual."

"Sex scandals?"

"On all teams there's some what screw around and some what don't, depends, but nobody's so stupid as to go looking for trouble. Come on, Marc, you know Butch; he's from my day, not yours. He runs a tight ship. Verne Sullivan is even worse. Thanks for the training tips." He turned and went back the way they had come, through the only door into the gym.

Marc followed him out, but instead of turning left, he headed for Butch Bello's office. Though he would have a long wait, he might as well take it easy, maybe even write a short piece on training methods, how baseball conditioning differed from football. A think piece for the Sunday supplement. He began composing the article in his head.

It was a long walk to Bello's office—the manager wasn't kidding when he said if anybody wanted to cry on his shoulder, he'd get lots of exercise—through the darkest, least-used section of the light-green main corridor, its monotony broken only by the colored rectangles marking entrances to the various rooms and passages off the corridor. The doors to these rooms were set back in recesses about three feet deep so they would not obstruct the corridor when they were opened out, and they were painted to match their concrete niches. Marc went from the team area, identified by its beige doors with a sprinkling of blue office entrances, into the section of the corridor that held the long line of gray supply-room doors on both sides of the wide corridor. Lost in thought, he passed the yellow door of the owner's private elevator on his right, then the red fire-stair door, its passage to the street lighted by a faintly glowing red exit sign. Immediately after the exit passage, at the black entrance of the first equipment-storage room, he automatically turned left into the dim last tunnel on the home-team side—the one leading to the right side of the outfield—in which Butch Bello's office was situated. Eyes blinded by the brilliance of the opening to the brightly lighted playing field only sixty feet away, it wasn't until he was almost at the niche framing the green door of Bello's office that he looked down and saw the body. The *body*? Samuel Moultran Prager, in a charcoal-black suit, lying on his left side across the dark passage, crumpled on the concrete floor just outside the office, his right temple crushed in, with a roundish, bloody, baseball-size depression. Prager's right foot was just within the recess, his left hand stretched out, pointing toward the far wall.

The bloodstained baseball was on the concrete floor, about six feet farther away, resting against the right-hand wall.

8

"What the devil are you doing that far from where you're supposed to be?" Julius Witter yelled. "You owe me another story, remember?"

Marc moved the phone receiver farther from his ear and whispered, "Not so loud, Julius—do you want everybody to hear? There are people walking past all the time."

"You're outdoors? In the street? Have you lost your mind?"

"I wanted to get away from the Gruber Dome. Remember what happened when I called you about the Super Bowl murder? I don't need the police trying to pin it on me again and using me for bait."

There was a moment's hesitation, then Witter's voice took on a conspiratorial air. "Another murder?" he asked in a half whisper. "Excellent. Start dictating, I'll take it down."

"Actually, I was thinking of going to the *News* or the *Post* with this. I've gotten the feeling lately that you don't appreciate me, Julius. I could start at either paper with a lot more money than I'm getting from *The Sentry*."

"You're holding me up again, Burr? After all I've given you already?"

"You haven't given me anything, Julius; all you've done is bring me up to what some of the others are getting. Which hasn't made up for fifteen years of keeping me at Guild minimum. But I'm willing to forgive you. All I want is what I know you're able to give:

twenty-five a week now and another twenty-five if the story runs for three days.''

Witter sighed loudly. "It can't be done. If I break Mr. Heisenberg's ceiling for you, every reporter in the place will be screaming for a raise and I'll get fired. If they lost me, the sports section would rapidly go to hell. In all good conscience, I can't do such a terrible thing to *The Sentry*.''

"Not even for the greatest story of the year? With a guaranteed one-hour lead on the rest of the rags? You could have a full page on a special edition, Julius, exclusive to *The Sentry*, before anyone even knows what's happening. Think, Julius, there must be some way you could give me the lousy fifty a week. Twenty-six hundred a year won't break Heisenberg. And speed it up; every minute that passes is that much less time you'll be selling papers.''

"I assure you, Marc, there is no . . . Unless . . . No, no, that's too ridiculous to even contemplate.''

"What, Julius? Talk fast, I'm running out of quarters.''

"What crossed my mind . . . no matter what, I can't pay you more than the good reporters on the paper, but if I changed your category—''

"I will not work with Nelda Shaver, Julius. No way.''

"I wasn't thinking of . . .'' Witter's voice took on a full Shakespearean richness. "Marc, my boy, as your benevolent mentor, you know I've always had your best interests at heart, advancing your career—sometimes against my better judgment and always ignoring your obvious failings and your lack of respect for the profession—at a speed which others of similarly limited talent and skill might find breathtaking. What I am about to suggest, although you're clearly several decades away from having earned it, is that you might be jumped over all the others who are better qualified and be given the title of editor. Say, assistant weekend and night editor. No, no, don't thank me. Just give me the story.''

"Assistant coffee maker and gofer, you mean. Come on, Julius, don't con me. That's the kind of job you give the little interns from Columbia who still think journalism has some resemblance to what they were taught in school and whose job interviews consist of finding out how long their parents will continue to support them. But that is an idea. Tell me I'm now assistant sports editor.''

Witter choked, loudly, at a complete loss for words. When he caught his breath, he roared, "I don't need an assistant, especially an insolent, disrespectful, smart-ass, arrogant, presumptuous, ill-mannered, coarse, impudent—"

"Yeah, sure, Julius, we all know you have a big vocabulary. Read the *Post* one hour from now. Good-bye. And that's not a contraction for 'God be with you.' ''

"Wait, wait, don't hung up. It's possible that . . . I may be able to . . . it will take a good deal of effort and . . . very well, Burr. We will both regret this, I am sure, especially you, but I accept your proposal."

"Say it out loud, Julius, just to make sure there's no misunderstanding."

Marc heard the editor take a deep breath and let it out slowly. In measured words, he said, "Marcus Aurelius Burr is now promoted to the post of assistant sports editor. Under me. Now give me the story.''

"And the raise, Boss?''

"Raise? After being promoted? The title and the honor should be more than sufficient."

"What is the most you can raise an editor? Talk numbers.''

"You wretched greedy little money-grubber. You only asked for twenty-five and another twenty-five if the story ran three days. That's all you're going to get. Now cut out this foolishness and start dictating."

Marc knew it was time to stop, so he said, "At shortly after four P.M. this afternoon, Brooklyn Bandits manager Enzo 'Butch' Bello found the body of Samuel Moultran Prager, owner of the Bandits, lying dead on the gray concrete floor, face down, right outside the door of the manager's office in the dimly lit tunnel leading to right field. Prager's right temple had been crushed in by a bloody official National League baseball that was found near the body. Take it from there, Julius."

"Wait. It's only three o'clock now. How do you know Bello's going to find the body?"

"I have an appointment with him at his office for five after four, as soon as practice is over. Nobody ever goes into that part of the stadium unless it's to see Bello."

"Did you call the police?"

"I told you—I'm not gonna get burned twice. Let Bello call them."

"It would look funny if you got there after Bello did; a good reporter always gets there first."

"All right. I'll go back and watch practice and when Bello starts for the office, I'll go with him. But I'll let him walk a little ahead of me; I'll be damned if I find the body this time. The cops would skin me alive."

"Good. Call me as soon as the body is found, with a detailed report. How many pictures did you get?"

"Pictures?" Marc tried to sound innocent.

"You will persist in thinking you're near my level of intelligence. How many, Burr?"

"Six," Marc said resignedly.

"Only, six? Don't you put an empty roll in your camera when you go out on assignment? Just in case?"

"Sure, but it was sort of dark in the tunnel and the automatic flash went off. Very bright. I was afraid someone would notice."

"There was someone in the main corridor at the time?"

"I was afraid someone practicing in the field would see the flashes, and in the other direction, someone in the main corridor."

"Well, too late to change that. I'll send a messenger to pick them up from you."

"We didn't make a deal on the pictures, Julius. I was figuring on selling them to *Time*."

"Have you no loyalty, Burr? Editors are management, not labor. Doesn't the honor—"

"Twenty-five and twenty-five, Julius. And I am loyal; they're worth a lot more."

"You know I can't give you two raises in one day."

"Stop struggling, Julius; I want to give Dahliah the kind of home she deserves when we get married. Twenty-five tomorrow and twenty-five on Tuesday. That way it won't interfere with my other raises."

"Agreed," Witter said, giving up. "I'll have the messenger meet you near the Boomers' dugout."

"The cartridge will be in a large box. I don't want the messenger to tie me in with finding the body. He could sell the story to the *National Enquirer*."

"Do you think everyone is as venal as you are, Burr?"

"No, just the people who work for *The Sentry*. Where do you think I learned it from, mentor?"

9

It was three-thirty when Marc got back to the Gruber Dome. The area around the Dome was not the sort of place where stationery stores would normally hang out and he was reduced to buying a big tube of toothpaste to get a box that would hold the cartridge yet be small enough to pass on invisibly to Witter's messenger. He hoped. He also bought a box of antirattling tissues, a roll of Scotch tape, a package of wrapping paper, and another cartridge of film, in case the police—he just *knew* it would be Lieutenant Danzig from Homicide —decided to ask why Marc was carrying a camera without any film in it—Danzig was not really smart, but he was very shrewd—so what did Marc do with the pictures he took when he found the body and why didn't he call the police right away and was he aware of the penalties for withholding evidence from the police and . . . and . . . and . . . ? And when *The Sentry* came out with six—count 'em, *six*—pictures of the body on the front page before Danzig even got to the scene of the crime, it would be obvious to him that Marc was guilty, maybe not of murder (and maybe *yes* of murder; Danzig had no moral objection to framing *anybody* to close a case) but of *something*—it didn't matter what— something that would enable Danzig to hang Marc by his thumbs so that Marc would do anything Danzig wanted.

It would have been smarter, much smarter, to just walk away, not to find the body, not to take the pictures, not to call Witter, not to. . . But if he had done that, if he had played it smart, he would

never have had the chance to become an investigative reporter—or
even an assistant editor—he would never make enough money to
buy a brownstone, never marry Dahliah and then, one day, she'd
meet a nicer, richer, more successful, handsomer, taller . . . Oh,
Dahliah, the things I do for love of you.

Then there was the problem of finding a place dark enough and
private enough to take the film cartridge out of the camera and put
in the new one—must remember to snap some shots of the players—
a place where he could wrap the cartridge in tissues and seal the box
securely. And unseal it again, this time remembering to wipe his
fingerprints off the cartridge and the box and the tape and the
wrapping paper and—he was sure he forgot something—because it
was not beyond Julius Witter to save the evidence in case he decided
to turn Marc in, which Julius would eagerly volunteer to do to save
his own skin, or to save the price of an aspirin—Danzig gave people
big headaches—or even just to reduce the budget of the sports
department.

Marc paced up and down near the visiting team's dugout, looking
for Witter's messenger. Was it possible that the guy had already
been there and, impatient, not finding Marc, had left? Unlikely.
Short of flying, he could not have gotten there very much sooner
than Marc had. Some of the players were beginning to watch him;
soon there would be crude remarks about his having a thing for
baseball players, remarks to be remembered under Danzig's ques-
tioning, when all Marc wanted to this time was total invisibility or,
failing that, complete anonymity.

Then—God, could it be?—yes it could. A beautiful young
woman, one of the interns—he remembered seeing her slithering
around the newsroom—came across the field from the Bandits'
side, right across the infield, stopping all action dead. She swayed
with each high-heeled step like a mesmerized cobra, fixing one
hundred pairs of keen eyes, jiggled right up to Marc. Wearing a
tight, bright-red dress. *Red!* She walked right up to the paralyzed
Marc and threw her arms around him. "The package," she whispered conspiratorially into his ear, making it look as though she

were breathing passionately, doing her best to excite Marc. And succeeding.

"Huh?" Marc whispered, looking guilty of something.

"The pictures. Mr. Witter said. The cartridge," she explained, sounding irritated at his obtuseness. "You're supposed to slip it to me. In my tote bag. Secretly." She obligingly pressed herself against him even more tightly and wiggled sideways to present the tote bag to his right hand.

His arms went around her, unconsciously, to keep her from further vibration, but she took this as a signal that he wanted her to press closer. It wasn't possible, but she tried, she really tried.

"It's, uh, in my inside right breast pocket," he gasped.

"Get it," she whispered urgently. "I can't keep this up much longer. It's too humiliating and it's making a sex object of me. You're doing it purposely. Get it. Now!"

Marc tried to get his left hand in between them to reach his inside right breast pocket, he really tried, but her—she—they—were in the way. "Stop that immediately!" she ordered. Marc stopped immediately, his hand entangled in the red dress. "I'm going to report this to the Guild," she whispered. "And to the EEO Commission. Take your hand away. Now! This is overt sexual harassment and I'm going to sue you and the paper."

"I can't," Marc whimpered.

"If you can't control yourself, I'll hit you with my tote bag right in front of everybody. Hard."

"No. Don't. I can, but I can't. I mean I'm stuck. If you'll move away, just move away a little—" She moved back a full foot, looking at him with loathing. "Not that far—you have to shield me." She stayed where she was, glaring at him, daring him to grab her, to hold her closely again. Marc glanced around. Everyone in the stadium was staring at him, waiting, silent. Witter did this, Marc knew with a portion of his mind. Julius Witter. Deliberately. Witter did it to humiliate him, to get even with him for winning the promotion, to give him an inkling of what was to come from his Pyrrhic victory—"Another such victory over the Romans, and we are undone" came to this mind—and to make sure that when asked by Danzig, Witter could fake reluctance and be forced to explain how Marc had—over Witter's earnest good-citizen's protestations—insisted he take the photos secretly instead of turning them over to the police. Secretly? Ha! Witter had probably picked this Fury—undoubtedly from Nelda Shaver's staff—only because she was wearing this flaming-red dress.

Marc took the shiny bright-green package—it was the only wrapping paper the store had—out of his right breast pocket and held it out to the woman. She scornfully refused to touch it and turned slightly so that he could put it into the tote bag himself, flinching exaggeratedly as his hand came near her. The secret drop successfully made, she flounced off the way she had come, straight across the infield to the tunnel next to the Bandits' dugout. As soon as she had disappeared into the dark hole, Forrest Wade, the Boomers' star pitcher, who had been standing closest to Marc throughout the frolic, said, "If she's the professor you been dating, Burr, let me know what class she teaches. I'd sure lo-o-o-ove to take lessons from her."

His face as red as the dress, Marc walked rapidly across the field to the Bandits' dugout. He stuck his head down and yelled, "Hey, Butch, it's almost four. How about that interview you promised?"

Bello was conferring with Verne Sullivan. "I'm not finished yet," he said mildly. "I told you a little after four. Won't be much longer. You want to wait in my office, you're welcome."

Appalled at the thought of being the first to discover the body, Marc said, "I'll just hang around here and watch. Get me when you're ready." He took out his little camera—mustn't forget to take half a roll, at least—and stood on the first base line, aiming at the batter's box. Mario Demarco, the Bandits' leading slugger and star outfielder, was taking his swings. Granted, the pitcher wasn't putting much on the ball, but it still was an impressive performance. Ball after ball went into the left-field stands, pulled by Demarco close to the foul pole, where the distance was shortest. The Boomers have four great hitters, Marc thought, but the Bandits aren't exactly helpless either. Marc took some great shots, once catching the batter exactly in the middle of his swing, when the bat met the ball.

Demarco was followed by third baseman Alvin Smootra, not a great fielder, but an excellent leadoff man. Smootra held the bat very short and was dropping low Texas Leaguers into all fields at will, just beyond the reach of the infielders and well inside of what the outfielders could reasonably reach. When one of the outfielders moved in, Smootra popped one over his head and hooted as the outfielder scrambled back, trying to gauge the rebound as the ball rolled to the fence and to keep the hit down to a double. For his last swing, Smootra pushed a fast grounder into what would have been the hole between first and second had the second baseman run over to cover a steal on a hit-and-run play. Marc got some good shots of Smootra too, when he felt a tap on his shoulder.

"OK, I'm ready now," Bello said. "Let's go. I can give you fifteen minutes, then I got to meet with some of the other coaches." He started walking to the far right-field tunnel. "What are you waiting for?" he said over his shoulder. "You coming or not?"

Marc hurried to get beside Bello—no sense arousing suspicion. "Is it OK if we start talking now?"

"Sure, but don't ask me nothing about what I'm going to do tomorrow."

"How about off the record? You know my word is good."

"After we get in the office, not on the field." Bello's short bandy legs carried him along a lot faster than anyone would have expected and Marc had to hurry to keep up with the burly manager.

"Are you planning to start Warren Lamburt in the Series, Butch?"

"I'll use him when I think the time is ripe."

"I hear his arm's gone bad."

"Yeah? Well I never heard that. Why don't you ask the guy who gave you that bullshit for the details?"

"Come on, Butch, level with me."

"You ask me questions I could answer, you get answers. Ask me bullshit, you get bullshit."

"OK." They had reached the entrance to the last tunnel. "Who's calling the shots in the Series, you or Prager?"

Butch Bello turned and looked at Marc angrily. "You looking for a fat lip, Burr?" Marc flinched. "I'm the manager and I call the shots."

"What if Prager sends down a message telling you to do something?"

"He's the owner. He can make any decision he wants about the team, but he don't tell me how to manage."

"He's done it before."

Bello's face got redder. "Not in the World Series he don't. If we're gonna have a chance to win the Series, it gotta be done my way. He don't like it, he can get himself a new manager right in the middle of the World Series. Ha! Fat chance. Even Prager ain't that stupid."

"Can I quote you on that?"

"What are you, an asshole or something? I got enough problems with him without going public. I handle it my way, and I can pull it off. You try to make trouble and you'll spoil everything. Now come on." He turned back to the tunnel. "Let's get this over with."

Butch strode off into the tunnel, Marc following close behind. Their eyes took a few seconds to adjust from the bright lights in the Dome to the dim lighting in the tunnel, so they were almost on top of the body when Butch stopped suddenly. "Mamma mia," Butch swore, reverting to his childhood oath.

"Prager," Marc exclaimed. "It's Prager. He's been beaned."

Butch kneeled down and felt Prager's throat. "He's dead." He stood up. "Call the police. And an ambulance. I'll stay here so nobody touches nothing."

Marc tried to step over the corpse's legs, but Butch stopped him. "Where you going?"

"Into your office. To phone."

"I had it taken out last month; too much bitching over the phone. Go to the ones in the hall."

"You go," Marc said, taking out his little camera. "I want to take some pictures." He got a good one of Bello glaring at him over the body, and another of the manager running down the tunnel to the main corridor. Plus some good shots from a lot of good angles, of the body. This time he wasn't worried about the bright flashes being seen.

10

"You again?" Lieutenant Harvey Danzig exploded. "Didn't I tell you already before not to make any more trouble for me in Brooklyn?" He still looked like a soft, middle-aged accountant, as Marc remembered him, but an *angry* soft middle-aged accountant. A dangerous, angry, *mean* accountant. Where the hell was the messenger that Marc had phoned for right after Bello had come back? A *male* messenger, not Miss What's-her-name in the red dress—*Ms.* What's-her-name—to pick up the cartridge with the new photos on it, including two of Butch Bello standing near the body of Sam Prager. The little camera was burning hot in Marc's pocket. "Why'd you want to make trouble for me, Burr? Don't you know how many cases I got already in Brooklyn?"

"I didn't want to—that is, I didn't make trouble, Lieutenant." Marc quailed as the dim light in the tunnel flashed off Danzig's gold wire-framed glasses, right into his eyes. "All I did was—I *didn't*. Butch Bello found the body."

"Keep looking at the body, Burr, when I talk to you. Not at me. When I want you to look at me, I'll let you know." Marc obediently dropped his eyes to the corpse of Slippery Sam Prager, halfway down the tunnel. "I already talked to Bello. He says you were right with him when you found the body." He took off his glasses and put his face tightly close to Marc's. "You going to start by lying to me?"

"Start? No, sir, I'm not going to start—that is, not just not *start*,

69

I'm not going to—even later— Anytime." He collapsed into confusion. "What I mean is," he said slowly, "is that I'm telling you the truth. I was way behind Butch when *he* found the body."

"Bello says you were right next to him. When I find out which one of you is lying, I'm going to sweat you until I find out why."

"Sweat me? No. Sweat Butch. I'm not lying, Lieutenant. Honest. And don't tell Butch I told you to sweat . . . he gets very upset when . . . Butch isn't lying, not really; he's just exaggerating. He couldn't even tell how far behind him I was; his back was turned."

"He says you sent him away. He says he told *you* to call the police and you sent him away. Why? What did you take off the body while he was gone?"

"Nothing. I didn't . . . I wouldn't even touch . . . all I did was . . . wasn't. Nothing."

"You just stood there? For five minutes? With the body? Looking?" Danzig sneered. "You can't even keep your eyes on him now, with me around, and you're telling me you stood there for five minutes, alone, and just watched the dead body? With his head bashed in? And the blood?"

Marc looked around frantically. Where was Witter's messenger? Where was *everybody*? Why didn't he have hundreds of witnesses to see how he was being treated? Danzig noted the desperation in Marc's eyes. "Nobody's coming, Burr. It's just you and me, kid, for the next ten minutes. Bello is with a stenographer right now making a statement and everybody else is kept away from the scene. Now, tell me some more lies."

"Actually I wasn't looking at the—him. I just wanted to make sure nobody touched—moved anything—stole the ball. The evidence."

"You're so stupid, Burr, you can't even lie good. I got kids right here in Brooklyn, little kids, never been picked up before for anything, could give me a better story than that right off, first time they get nabbed. Who don't have a college education. Dropouts. Don't they teach you *anything* in college?" He leaned against the concrete wall casually. "Why couldn't Butch Bello watch the evidence while

70

you went to make the call? That way, right after you called nine-one-one, you could've called your office and gotten the story in ahead of everybody else. Or even called your office *before* you called nine-one-one, knowing how you operate.''

''Why, I—that is—I didn't want to leave Bello alone with the body. After all—''

''What makes you think Bello did it?''

''I didn't say—''

''Sure you did. Otherwise, why couldn't you leave him alone with the body?''

''I never said Bello—All I meant was—It had to be a baseball player, a pitcher, and Bello's smart, even if he looks like—Whoever beaned Prager, it must have been—*could* have been—one of the Bandits' star pitchers and Butch wouldn't want him to be arrested. He needs all his players to have a chance to win the Series and he's never won a Series in his whole career, which is very important to him. So I figured—actually I didn't figure anything, it was more sort of unconscious—that it would ruin the evidence for the police—for *you*—if he wiped the fingerprints off the ball, maybe even threw away the ball. To save the team. To win the Series.''

''You wanted *me* on this case?''

''Why—well, of course. Yes. Certainly. You did such a good— terrific—job on the Super Bowl murder that . . . I mean . . . What I mean is, you're *experienced*.''

''So why didn't you tell Bello to call me instead of just nine-one-one? Or when he got back, why didn't you call me, tip me off, that we got a big case here, could get me lots of publicity? Or did you want to save me a big headache with another impossible job—you know how many cases I got?—which could land me in the shit for not closing a murder with such a prominent citizen–type victim.'' He smiled evilly. ''All right, Burr, enough horseshit. What did you take off the body? A diary? An address book? What?''

''Nothing. Honest. You could search me.''

''OK, thanks for the invitation. Palms on the wall and spread 'em.''

"No. I didn't mean—it was just a figure of speech."

"I could make believe I didn't hear that last part, but I don't need to. If I take you downtown on suspicion, or even as a witness, you think I couldn't frisk you? Accidentally? So save us both the trouble, huh?"

Marc gave up. He wouldn't have been able to sell these pictures to Witter anyway. "I took some pictures. Of the body." Danzig held out his hand. "No," Marc protested. "You have no right." Danzig's hand was still out, not reaching, just waiting for Marc to put the camera in it. "They're my private property. For *The Sentry*." The hand was still out, patiently. "Look, Lieutenant, your technical people will be here in a little while. They have good equipment; this is just a little auto-focus. Not really very sharp. Practically a toy. Cheap lens. Slow shutter. I didn't move anything, I swear—just took some shots. Come on, Lieutenant, give me a break."

Danzig's hand was still out. "OK, Lieutenant," Marc said, trying harder, "tell you what I'm going to do. I didn't tell you before, but I've been promoted to assistant editor of the whole sports department. I'm in a position to give you a big buildup, a real *big* buildup, on this case. I'm going to take all the remaining shots on the roll of you. Here. Now. With the body. Looking real good. Doing detective things. We'll spell your name right and everything. Say what a great job you did on the Super Bowl murder. Maybe even say you ought to be considered for chief of detectives or whatever the next step up for you is. What do you say?"

"A big buildup?" The hand was withdrawn. Marc nodded eagerly and took the camera out of his pocket. "You check with me before you print anything about me? I don't want this to look like a setup, you understand." Marc nodded again and began snapping pictures. Danzig took his hat off, walked over to the body, and looked down, serious, changing his pose each time the flash went off. "How do I know it shows what you say you took, that there's nothing else important on it? That you're not conning me?"

"I'll give you the uncut roll as soon as it's developed. You'll see some shots of the players on it, then the shots of the body, and of Butch with the body, then the shots I'm taking of you right now. Uncut. That way you'll know. You can even use it as evidence. If anyone asks me, I'll say I never told you about it, I forgot, then when I remembered, I turned over the roll to you."

"OK, but I still got to talk to you."

"I told you everything I know."

"You don't even know what you know, kid. When I get through with you, you'll remember stuff you wouldn't believe. We're gonna meet tomorrow morning, early, say eight o'clock. Just you and me. You hand over the film and we talk for a while, while we eat."

"Where?" Marc was resigned.

"You're kidding," Danzig said, smiling. "My usual place, your favorite. The best diner in Brooklyn; you know where it is. Now they know—that waitress, she never forgets a regular, especially when he tips good like you do—she knows exactly what you like and how you like it. Just don't tell nobody else about it, kid; I want to keep it exclusive."

11

"You realize, of course," Julius Witter remarked, "that you did everything wrong, everything, in the worst possible way." His supercilious smile was genuine, for once, with no thought of hiding his satisfaction.

"I did everything in the best possible way," Marc said defensively, "under the circumstances. I had to make decisions immediately, on the spur of the moment. In real time."

"Of course, but you should have realized that, given your limited intelligence, and your lack of experience—"

"I've had fifteen years of experience as a reporter," Marc retorted, "plus—"

"You've put in fifteen years, but even working under me, even with all the opportunities you've had to model yourself on your betters, at the first inkling of something that couldn't be handled routinely, you let your greed and your animal instincts take over. Instead of trying to dredge up some slight memory of what I've tried to teach you, you bulled ahead blindly and—"

"What would you have done in my place?"

"I? I would not have put myself in your place to begin with—that's what I'm trying to make you see. In every pattern of action there is a fork which, if chosen without a full appreciation of the consequences—"

"Specifically?"

Witter looked at Marc with pity. "You don't even want to learn the general rules which govern . . . This younger generation wants only the quick fix. Well, I will not bow to the demands of the incompetent, the ignorant, and the inept. I will, instead, remind you of the ramifications of your condition so that you may consider, if you are capable of concentrating your mind fully on the hopelessness of your situation, what possible alternative there may be, if any, to immediate *seppuku*. Considered by the Japanese to be a particularly honorable form of suicide. Not here, please; this is an expensive carpet.''

"I was waiting for you to get to that suggestion, Julius. Why the big buildup?"

"Surely, after a hard day's work, am I not permitted a little pleasure? So, to put things in order, to clarify your thinking: Within minutes after Lieutenant Danzig let you go from the stadium, you came here and, sensibly, handed me the new photographs along with your clumsily written updated story. Equally sensibly—possibly, by then, you realized how desperate your circumstances were— you did not attempt to extort additional concessions from me. Within those same few minutes, Lieutenant Danzig surely saw the latest extra edition of *The Sentry* with your story and your original six photographs on the front page. In spite of the normal business precaution of releasing the story under my own byline, Danzig knew it was you who broke the story and took the photographs. He is not an intelligent man, but neither is he a complete fool. So this evening—between two A.M. and four A.M. is the favored time of the KGB—there will be a knock on your door and the minions of the law will hail you to your just desserts.''

"I already have an appointment with him tomorrow morning.'' Marc slumped in his chair. The euphoria he had felt after he had exacted the promotion and the raise from Witter had long since faded.

"Ah, then he's toying with you. Typical. Did it ever occur to you that, had you just phoned me the story and given me the photographs, as was your job, instead of practicing extortion, all this could have been avoided? If you didn't want to be involved with

Danzig again which, given the—uh—interesting adventures you once shared with him, would have been a perfectly reasonable request, I would have sent one of our other reporters, a good, *loyal* reporter—we had five of them at the Gruber Dome today—who would have been happy to claim discovery of the body and to get his byline on an eyewitness exclusive story."

"I wanted—" Marc looked embarrassed—"I *needed* . . . it was for Dahliah. She deserves—"

"Are you now trying to hide behind a woman's skirts? For shame, Burr. I only hope that I and the paper will not have to give Danzig additional evidence against you to protect ourselves and our integrity."

"But you're the one who sent that sexpot in the red dress to the stadium."

"She was the only responsible person available in Sports on such short notice and you had better be careful what you call her. She doesn't like to be called a sexpot or reminded, in any way, during working hours—quite properly, I might add—that there are two sexes. Were she a true sexpot, I doubt that Nelda Shaver would have hired her. Nelda is quite jealous of her prerogatives as queen of 'The Sporting Woman' page. And I too think very highly of the young lady you are unwarrantedly maligning. I predict a great future for her. Within a very short time you will see, as a byline on some highly important investigative stories, the name of Lucy Stone Valentine."

"Nelda Shaver? *Lucy Stone* Valentine? Her mother named her after . . . ? Oh, my God! She said she was going to sue me for sexual harassment. And *The Sentry*, too."

"Sue *The Sentry*? Because of you? Do you realize that if she sues the paper, she may even—you know how lawyers are—do something much worse. She may even sue *me*. After all, I had just promoted you. Whatever did you do to her, Burr? And why did you do it? Can't you keep your mind on your work, even on a baseball field? Have you no reverence for The Great American Game? What will Dahliah say? How can you possibly explain that to her? No, don't answer; your personal problems are really not very interesting, except as they affect our circulation.'' Witter took out his handkerchief and wearily wiped his bald head. ''No, Burr, I'm afraid there's no way out of it; you'll have to swear you were not in the stadium at the time or, at least, not there on official business. Perhaps if I fired you retroactively . . . ? No, that would never stand up in court; you're such an incompetent liar. Were there any witnesses?''

''At least a hundred, Julius, and I was there on important official business. Which is what I was doing with *her*. *Sentry* business, on which *you* sent her. And there are the photos, on the front page, for proof. My fate is tied to yours, Julius, and the paper's.''

Witter took a deep breath. ''Yes, very well then, I shall try to arrange . . . Nelda is the only one in a position to control that ambitious, litigious little—young woman. That is, I hope Nelda will be able to induce her to . . . persuade her, that is, that it would be advantageous to . . . in the suddenly promising career, which you, Burr, have opened to her. Yes, you will have to go to Nelda, apologize for your uncontrollable lusts, of course, and ask her, nicely . . . Do you understand, Burr?''

''Tell Nelda that I have uncontrollable lusts? *Nelda?* I'm not going to do it, Julius.''

''The propitious time,'' Witter went on, completely ignoring Marc's protest, ''would be tonight, at Nelda's home, of course, when she's relaxed, vulnerable. Relatively. Strike while the iron's hot, eh, Burr? But unfortunately, I have other things for you to do.''

''Now? It's late and Dahliah specifically told me to be on time tonight. It's Friday, in case you've forgotten. Everyone else in the Toy Shop has gone home.''

''They're reporters, Marc my boy, and you're now an editor. We editors have no hours, you know. Or days. Always on call, like the conscientious healers of old.''

Marc knew when he was beaten. Again. ''What do you want me to do?'' he asked.

''The proper attitude, Marc my boy. Keep it up, and who

knows . . . ?'' Witter turned businesslike. "I truly appreciate your willingness to help these tired old shoulders shed another burden, one which a man of your age can . . . with no trouble . . . You'll love it, I'm sure. A real challenge. You will have a whole page to edit, all by yourself. Our most popular feature: 'The Sporting Woman.' Congratulations again, my boy, This is your day of days.''

"Edit Nelda? She doesn't need editing, she needs a course in remedial writing. And elementary journalism. All she has is gossip, clothes, who's screwing whom, and the latest color that's *in* of the pom-poms you sew on to your tennis socks.''

"You must learn to be more tolerant of your colleagues, Marc, particularly those whom Mr. Heisenberg favors. We charge double our normal rate for advertisements on Nelda's page and the page opposite, yet advertisers fight viciously for the right to buy more space. Mr. Heisenberg admires and respects the talents and skills that produce such universal admiration and income.''

"Skills? She's illiterate. Her mind is a sewer filled with soap-opera situations, toilet-bowl-cleaner ads, and sex scandals.''

"Exactly. Which makes her so popular with our readers.''

Marc was still struggling. "I can't work with her. She's almost never in the office.''

"She says she does her best work in bed, and who am I to say her nay? It is no hardship.''

Marc stood up and glared down at Witter. "I've changed my mind, Julius. I'll go back to being a reporter.''

Witter tried to look regretful. "Normally, Burr, I would be glad to accept that offer to reduce the payroll, but it's not possible. I've already hired a reporter to take your place.''

"Take my place? A new reporter? You can't; I've got fifteen years' seniority.''

"You used to have seniority, Burr, but as an editor, you have less than one day's time in. Of course, if you want to resign from the paper . . .''

Marc sat down and put his head in his hands. "I have Danzig on my back, and tomorrow he'll kill me about the pictures and for not telling that I found the body. I still have to produce a column three times a week. I still have to go out and bring in stories every day. Four stories. I have to get in good with Nelda Shaver so that intern of hers won't sue me. I have to edit Nelda's page, which means teach her how to write, and see her every day. In her boudoir. Which if Dahliah ever finds out . . ."

"May I point out, Marc, that all of this is exactly what you asked for? Didn't you read fairy tales when you were little? You have to be very careful with your three wishes."

Marc put his head down on the desk, the cool wood. "The new reporter, Julius, the one you hired, did he fill out his forms yet or do I have to show him how?"

"Not hired, Marc, promoted. From intern. Not him—her. A very promising young woman. Lucy Stone Valentine."

12

There was a big plate of Marc's favorite fall food, stir-fried tofu, covered with Dahliah's special hoisin-and-scallion sauce, now cold, brown, and desiccated, alongside of which was a bowl of limp room-temperature crisp-fried string beans and a cut-glass bowl of fruit salad. Plus a bottle, unopened, thank God, of sparkling cider, also room temperature—but there was always ice, wasn't there? The candles in their low ceramic holders had dripped themselves into pink-and-white stalagmites rising from the newly ironed red-checked bistro tablecloth. Dahliah, looking lovely in a velvety green gown he had never seen before, was sitting opposite him at the table, where she had clearly been sitting for some hours—the dress, even to Marc's untutored eye, having lost its freshness—reading the first page of a book over and over. Marc sensed immediately that Dahliah was not happy with him. "I did call," he offered apologetically.

She put her finger on the page to hold her place—the first line, Marc noted—and looked at him with less-than-glowing love, but calmly, calmly. "Yes, you did. Perfect timing. Just as I was taking the Szechuan Hot and Spicy Tofu off the stove, perfectly cooked, ready to serve you as soon as you walked in."

"I told you I might be a little late."

"In the overall scheme of things, three hours is but the flicker of a thought in the God Mind, but in my trivial little arrangements, you bastard . . . After a hard day's work teaching cops who aren't the least bit interested in criminal psychology, and after running all over Ninth Avenue to find all the ingredients and after spending hours to find the perfect dress for tonight and slaving over a hot . . . I especially told you to be on time tonight. Twice.''

"I know, it's Friday night and you like—we like—to make it sort of special, but things happened today that—good things—that you'll be happy to—"

"*Friday* night? *Sort* of special? You didn't even *remember*? Not even *flowers*?"

Marc searched his mind. Nothing. But there had to be something. Dahliah was usually rational, sensible, did not go off just for a minor . . . Usually. A jewel among women. Mustn't . . . "Remember? Of course I remembered, darling, but there was this murder that—"

"You did remember? OK. What day is today?"

"Today? Friday, of course, the beginning of a wonderful weekend. I was planning . . . We'll have two whole days together, just by ourselves, no interruptions, just the two of us. Go to a show—we have lots more money now; I'll tell you all about it right after I eat this delicious supper you made—and dining out and dancing and—"

"Today," she said, articulating each syllable exaggeratedly, "is the eve of the first anniversary of the day I made the fatal mistake of moving in here with you."

"Well, yes, of course, I knew *that*," Marc said quickly, "but I was so anxious to come home to you that I figured it was more important to—"

"*Anxious?* It's ten-thirty!"

"I had to work late on the murder. Witter insisted. It's part of the new job. How I got that big raise." He knew he was babbling but he couldn't stop now. "To buy a building all for ourselves. Our own home. For you. I did it all for you. Entirely for you."

"*Murder?*" She did a double take. "You said *murder*?" She closed the book. A good sign, Marc thought. Probably. She stared at him suspiciously. Worriedly? Yes, that too, but more of the suspiciously. "What are you talking about?"

"Yes, well, you probably didn't see the paper, what with being so rushed and all making this terrific first-anniversary party and buying that beautiful dress. Gown." He paused and took her hand. "We're really very lucky, you know. Lots of couples don't last this long. These days. It shows something. Character. Dependability. Reliability. Empathy. Understanding. Of each other's problems. Real understanding. Love. *True* love. Which will probably last forever. Especially after we're married. And trust," he added, thinking of Lucy Stone Valentine's threat and the close contact he would be forced into with Nelda Shaver. In her apartment. Which Dahliah was sure to find out about. "Lots of trust."

"What murder?" she repeated obstinately.

"Samuel Moultran Prager." At her puzzled look, he added, "The owner of the Brooklyn Bandits. They're a baseball team. From Brooklyn." Dahliah didn't look any better educated than before. "The National League Champions. They're going to play in the World Series. For the World Championship. Against the Jersey Boomers. In Brooklyn. Tomorrow."

"Tomorrow? Saturday? On our anniversary?"

"Well, yes. It's . . . they didn't do it deliberately. It just happened to work out that way. Coincidentally. Because the Bandits"—he prayed God would forgive the lie—"took seven games to win the National League pennant. You understand."

"I understand? I do *not* understand!"

"Well, yes, I know you're not very interested in sports, but I don't mind. Most women are not—professionals, I mean, who have their own careers, which is very laudable—and have enough to do cooking anniversary meals and buying green dresses. Gowns. Beautiful green gowns. After work. I don't mind. Not really. Maybe, after we're married, if you want to ask me some questions, I'll be glad to—"

"You'll be working tomorrow? Saturday? On our anniversary? Our *first* anniversary? You said you were planning a whole celebration weekend for us."

"Well, yes, of course. Right after the game. As soon as the game

82

is over and I can write the stories, that is. It's the first game of the Series and I have to be there. Especially now that I've been promoted. It's very important, opening day of the Series. No way I can get out of it. But right after I send in—"

"Then we'll have Saturday night and all day Sunday together, at least? Without interruptions? To celebrate?"

"Saturday night and Sunday morning? Certainly. Then right after the second game—"

"The *second game*? How many games are there?"

"Actually, there's no way of knowing. As soon as one of them wins four games . . ." Dahliah glared at him, "There can't be more than seven," he said very quickly, "but there are lots of people who are sure—betting heavily, *very* heavily—that the Boomers win it in four."

"Seven days? The whole anniversary *week*? Our second honeymoon? Killed? For *baseball*? And you want me to *marry* you?"

"Four days, maybe," Marc said desperately. "It could easily be only four days. The Boomers are the best sluggers—that is, they hit . . . You see, in baseball . . . Actually, four days is five days; there's a travel day—even though they're just across the river. Between the second and third games they leave another day, for traveling, so even if they win in four, it takes five days. That's all. Just five days. If they win in four. Of course, you shouldn't take that as a firm . . . I don't *control* . . . If the Boomers don't win in five games, between the fifth and the sixth games . . ." He realized he was babbling again. In panic.

"*Nine* days?" Now Dahliah was really upset. "It could take *nine* days? *Both* weekends? In a row?"

"Highly unlikely. *Very* highly unlikely. *Extremely* . . . Well, it's possible, *barely* possible, but . . ." He stopped and looked miserable. Nothing more to say. His fate was in her hands.

She took pity on him. No woman could resist a man in such trouble. "Do you want me to heat up the tofu? Maybe if I added a little water, it would unshrivel."

"No, no." Marc seized the reprieve and picked up his chopsticks. "Don't bother. I'm starving and it looks delicious. Absolutely delicious. And maybe after . . . ?"

"Not tonight; I'm not in the mood anymore. Let's have a relaxing evening—you can tell me all about your raise and your promotion—and tomorrow we can spend the whole morning in bed. What time does the game start? How long before it starts do you have to be there?"

"Oh," Marc said casually, "didn't I tell you? I must have forgotten to mention it. I have an appointment tomorrow morning. Early. With Lieutenant Danzig."

13

"Why do we have to meet in this diner?" Marc asked, as Danzig, fifteen minutes late, walked up to the front entrance.

"It's the best diner in Brooklyn," Danzig explained. "You want to eat at the second best?" He waited until Marc pulled open the door, then pushed past him.

"I didn't mean that. I meant, suppose someone I know—there are some politicians I recognized going in—suppose someone sees me with you. He'll think I'm—that I might be involved in the Prager killing."

"I don't want you to even mention about that till after I eat, Burr. You trying to spoil my appetite or something? Get me all upset? 'Cause if that's what you want . . ." He stopped suddenly and looked over the room.

"No, no, not at all." Marc twisted frantically to keep from bumping into Danzig. "Why are we waiting? There are lots of empty booths."

"For my regular table. Where nobody can hear what I'm saying. There's guys all over got big mouths and as soon as they get collared, they try to make a deal, tell everything they know. You think I want the other guys at the house to get the credit for what I figure out? After all the work I put in?"

"Regular booth? But we've only been here once."

"You, maybe. Not me."

The corner table finally opened up and, as the hostess led them to their seats, Marc tried to figure how he could bury the tab—the best diner in Brooklyn also had the best prices—without Witter noticing. This breakfast, especially the way Danzig ordered, would cost more than Marc's raise for the week.

"I'll have a large orange juice," Lieutenant Danzig said, "fresh squeezed, not out of the pitcher. And the lox and bagel—a poppy-seed bagel, with a thick layer of Nova Scotia salmon, not the regular lox, sliced thin. A thin slice of Bermuda onion too, with some capers on the side. In a little bowl. And the Blue Mountain coffee, a mug, not a cup, fresh filtered, with a cheese Danish, and keep them both coming. Hot Danish, and a bowl of apricot jam, the good stuff, Sharon Valley, not the usual crap. You ever taste fresh-baked, hot cheese Danish with imported apricot jam, Burr? Fantastic. I'll give you a little taste of mine in case you want to order some for yourself. Now, what are you having?"

"How about the blintzes?"

"Good choice," Danzig said. "They make fantastic blintzes here." He addressed the waitress. "Give my host here a large order of blintzes. Blueberry blintzes. No, make that cherry. They got the best cherry blintzes in Brooklyn here, Burr, really fantastic. You'll love them. Better make that a double order, miss, I might take a taste myself too. With plenty of sour cream on the side. Bring him a pineapple juice to start, goes perfect with the cherry blintzes. They have the thick kind here, with pieces of pineapple in it, not from the can. And skim milk—right, Burr? That's your drink; I never forget a drink. And a prune Danish, just in case."

"All I wanted was a plain—"

"Nah, plain is for guys who don't know how to live. When you're with me, kid, you get the best. Especially for this meal."

"But I don't like prune Danish."

"OK, so I'll wrap it up and take it with me for later."

"You once told me you hated prune Danish."

"In the department, you learn to do things you don't like. Part of the job."

The waitress arrived with the juice. Mercifully.

Danzig leaned back, stuffed and satisfied, then leaned forward "You don't want this prune Danish, do you?" he asked Marc.

Marc waved it away, too full to talk. If Dahliah saw him now, she'd put him on bread and water for a month. Maybe not even bread, the way she'd looked at him as he left. He had tried to dress quietly, not to awaken her, but it was useless—the evils of a double bed—from the moment he slid out from under the blanket. She had watched every move closely and silently until he rang for the elevator. "Take your time writing the story of the game," she said solicitously, "so you can do a perfect job. We wouldn't want to displease Julius Witter, would we?" Solicitously? Ha! "Don't hurry home. Oh, and bring *The Times* with you when you come in." On Saturday night, the Sunday *Times* hit their neighborhood newsstands at about ten-thirty. Very funny, Dahliah. . . .

". . . lie to me?" Danzig asked quietly. Too quietly.

"I didn't lie to you," Marc said. "Everything I told you was true."

"Did you tell me you found Prager's body first. Did you tell me you took a set of pictures *before* you took the pictures I was on? Did you tell me you phoned your paper an hour before Bello called nine-one-one?"

"Well, no, but—"

"That's lying," Danzig said with finality. "Any argument?" Marc shook his head weakly. "You want to put it legal? How about withholding evidence? How about interfering with the police officers in the line of their duties? How about losing me an hour in apprehending the perpetrator? Don't you know that the most important time is right after the crime is committed? If I wanted, I could book you on a hundred charges, all legit. And that's if I decided to only tell the truth. If I wanted to give you a real hard time, you think I couldn't find a couple envelopes of coke on you? And a guy willing to turn state's evidence and finger you? Is that what you want?"

"All I was trying to—"

"You're not listening, Burr." Danzig gulped down Marc's left-over pineapple juice. "I could hang this whole thing on you and you're trying to give me bullshit excuses. Even your paper couldn't get you out of this one. Now tell me why I shouldn't take you in for murder and sweat you good."

"Because you know I didn't do it."

"What has that got to do with it? You were the last one to see Prager alive."

"Dead."

"Same thing—don't try to change the subject. You lied to me. You gave me a hard time. You took advantage of my good nature. You cost me an hour. I could have solved the case right off, and you screwed it up. What I asked you was, what are you going to do about it?"

"Apologize?"

"Not even step one."

"Promise not to do it again?"

"Burr, you really looking for trouble?"

"You want me to find the killer?"

"Nah, you're an amateur. I'll find the killer. All you got to do is ask around, which is your job anyway, find out stuff. I'll do the rest."

Marc put into words what he had been trying to avoid for the past hour: "You want me to be the bait?"

"Sure," Danzig said. "What else you good for? And to pick up information. People, especially the murderer, they're going to talk to you more than to me. With detectives, the murderer always clams up. With reporters, everybody wants to get his name in the papers."

"And report to you exclusively?"

"You maybe got somebody else in the department? A relative?"

"I still work for *The Sentry*. If I don't give them any information, they're going to wonder what I'm doing. Maybe even send me to cover weekend volleyball on Fire Island. That won't do you any good."

"Well, sure, you can tell them. *After* you tell me. You got my

88

private number. Just don't tell them the name of the killer until after I arrest him.''

"The name of . . . are you kidding?"

"Burr, you're always trying to make things complicated. And you got a very poor memory. Usually, most cases, everybody knows who the killer is, even the reporters. All I got to do is put on the pressure a little, push him a little, sweat him a little, until he cracks. Then I arrest him, sweat him *good,* get the confession, pick up the evidence after he tells me where it is, all the usual crap. Then I show him what I got, promise him anything he wants, put him in front of the TV for his confession like it's the first time, read him the Miranda, let him confess nice, and hand the package over to the D.A. Then, if he wants, I let him see his lawyer.''

"Aside from doing everything backward, there's only one trouble. I don't know who the killer is.''

"Don't tell me how to run my business; I got the best arrest-and-conviction record in the department. I don't have time to do it the hard way. You know how many cases I got? So don't bullshit me. You know, you really know, you just don't want to think simple. You like complicated.''

"Honest,'' Marc said wearily, "I *don't* know. I'm not protecting anybody.''

"Hey, I didn't say you were *protecting* the killer. I didn't even say you *know* that you know. All I said was . . .'' The waitress brought mugs of coffee, big mugs, for both of them. Marc started to push his away, then, what the hell—the condemned man's last supper—pulled it back and tasted it. Good, really good. And stimulating. The first time in a year he had had real coffee. He added cream guiltily, then, defiantly, a heaping spoonful of sugar. *White* sugar. If Dahliah found out . . . "Look,'' Danzig went on, "was Prager killed like what's-his-name said? The big fat guy who does publicity?''

"George Blondin? He's not all that fat. He used to be a great third baseman, not too long ago.''

"Yeah? Well, he tried to tell me it was an accident. Prager comes out of Bello's office and faints. He falls down, hits his head on a ball, which got in the exact right place accidentally, and bangs his brains out. Would you believe it?''

"It's his job to make the Bandits look good. And especially Prager. He wouldn't want anyone to think somebody wanted to kill Prager. Looks bad for the team ''

"OK. So it wasn't an accident, right?''

"There's no way. Anybody who knows baseball knows that Prager was beaned. Purposely. That ball was thrown *hard*.''

"OK. By one of his ex-wives?''

"By somebody with a good arm and a good eye.''

"A baseball player? Or an ex-baseball player?''

"OK, Danzig. I concede your point. A player, or a former player, with a good arm and a good eye, who was in the stadium at that time and was in the vicinity of the last tunnel on the right-field side at the time Prager was murdered.''

"So how many people was that?''

"Hard to say. Maybe fifty?''

"Maybe a lot less, believe me, but let's keep going. When was Prager killed?''

"Before three, when I found him. The blood—it was already dry. At least, it looked dry.''

"You a medical examiner, too, Burr? If I had got the M.E. there an hour earlier, we could have maybe pinned down the time of death a lot closer than what he said. You understand now why I got to hang you if I don't close this case fast?''

"Well, I'd see why you'd be maybe a little sore, but *hang* me? Why me?''

"Who else? If I don't get a murder first, at least I got an arrest and a conviction for *something*. Cold. Nothing personal, you understand—it's my job.'' Danzig looked like a very *cold-blooded* accountant now. "OK. Let's get back to business. So Prager was killed before two, maybe even before one. How much before?''

"What does the M.E. say?''

"Later. I want you to tell me first.''

"Well, it was probably after twelve. From the other stories I read, Butch Bello went to his office at about twelve, a little before, actually, and he came out a few minutes after. And he didn't report seeing any bodies.''

"You think he's telling the truth?''

Marc hesitated. "Probably, but I wouldn't want to bet my life on it. Why should he lie?''

"If he killed Prager himself . . . ?''

"Well, yes, but with Butch, it's more likely that he'd tear Prager's arm off if he really went out of control. And he wouldn't kill him right in front of his own office.''

"So you want to drop him from your list of suspects?''

Marc didn't have to think. "With the little I know right now, I wouldn't drop anybody. But if he did it . . . ? He was up in the owner's box all morning. With a dozen witnesses.''

"I never said Prager was killed before twelve, but even if he was, Bello never went out to the toilet? How long would it take him to go down to field level in the elevator? Or the stairs?''

"By elevator? Not very long—a minute or two. And there's a fire stair from the top deck—it's right off the main corridor near Bello's office—with a passage that leads out to the street. But before twelve? That's when the Boomers were practicing. Butch would have stood out like a pink elephant. The uniforms are a different color.''

"Did he have to go out on the field? Couldn't he have gone through the main corridor, seen Prager, and beaned him from where he was?''

"No. Impossible. Prager was hit on the right temple. If he was coming out of Bello's waiting room, the ball had to come from the field.''

"How do you know he was coming out? If he was going in . . .''

Marc was stunned. "I never thought of that. I just assumed that—''

"Yeah. Amateurs. If Prager was going *into* Bello's office, his right-hand side would be facing the main corridor. Bello comes along, sees Prager in a perfect position—these ballplayers move fast—throws the ball, hits Prager on the head, and takes off.''

"No, no, that doesn't sound right. Where does he get the ball?''

"What difference does that make? I'll find out when I sweat him. Picked it up in the corridor, maybe."

"There are no balls in corridors; ballplayers are too valuable to risk twisting their ankles. You think there was a ball lying exactly there, just waiting to be picked up and thrown? Forget it."

"OK, so he had it in his pocket. Details. Who cares? I checked up on Butch Bello first. He used to be a catcher with a terrific arm. He could easily have thrown the ball hard enough. Prager wasn't as young as he let on, and his bones weren't all that thick and hard."

"Bello is sixty. You think he could have aimed that perfectly? The light in there is very weak and he's throwing toward the field, which is well lit. Prager must have looked like a shadow from the corridor. To hit Prager, under those conditions, in *exactly* the right spot . . . ? If he missed—even if he *hit* Prager, but didn't kill him— Prager would have him in jail so fast . . . Managers play the odds; they don't take unnecessary risks like that."

"Yeah, but it's only thirty feet from the corridor to the office. Not that big a risk. Prager might not have been facing the right way to see Bello."

"Well, it's possible, but not very probable. Why'd you start with Bello?"

"It was right outside his office, wasn't it?"

"There are other things wrong with that scenario. First of all, it's not that easy to carry a baseball around in your uniform. It makes a big bulge and there's no reason to carry it—for the manager to carry it—and one of the coaches would have noticed. Verne Sullivan, for one. He's very sharp, never misses anything. Second, if Bello was carrying it, what for? In the hope of catching Prager outside his door, facing the right way, at exactly that second? How could he know Prager would be there? One second later and Prager's gone inside. The waiting-room door isn't locked. I know." Marc paused, thinking. There was something else bothering him. Danzig waited patiently. "Why did I assume that the ball was thrown from the field?" Marc spoke half to himself. "It wasn't just guesswork. There was a reason for . . . Yes. OK. I know. The ball. It was lying on the floor, against the wall. On the field side of Prager. Where it had bounced off after hitting him.''

"OK, so maybe Bello threw it from the field.''

"No. Can't be. I was watching him the moment he came out of the tunnel, waiting for him. He just walked out, period. I even went over, partway, to talk to him.''

"So you want to take Bello off the list now?''

Marc hesitated. "Not at this time. Not yet.''

"Did you notice''—Danzig looked smug—"you never even once mentioned motive?''

"I didn't?'' Marc said, flustered. "No, you're right, I didn't. I just assumed . . . You know more about this than I do. There must be a lot of money. Prager was rich. Very rich. Who inherits?''

"Forget about it. Anybody who inherits—his ex-wives or some other relatives—they wouldn't kill him this way. There's a hundred better ways, more professional, to knock him off. In fact, with his ex-wives, they're a lot younger than him and, with the alimony they get, all they got to do is wait. 'Course, I'm gonna have them checked out all the way, just for good luck, but forget it. Why else would anybody kill Prager? Sex?''

"Doubtful. He had a weakness for young blond girls, but he was smart enough to make sure they were old enough and single and unattached.''

"Not sex, not money, so what's left, Burr?''

"Fear? Hate?''

"That's what I figured. So who hated him?''

"Everybody, I guess. To know him was to hate him. Even I didn't like him very much, and I'm used to Julius Witter. Whom you've met.''

"OK, but who hated him *specially*? Enough to kill him?''

"Well, Bello, obviously. And George Blondin, the PR guy you mentioned before. Prager went out of his way to humiliate Blondin in public. Then there's Dan Zarik, the Boomers' manager. He was the manager for Prager once, when Bello was fired. Then he was bounced, on very short notice, when Bello was brought back.''

"That's all?"

"You know something I don't know? You tell me."

"I wasn't sitting on my ass yesterday like you. I told you—the time to solve a crime is right after it's been committed. But I want to hear it from you. Keep talking."

"Well, I might consider Verne Sullivan. He sort of took Bello under his wing when Butch was breaking into the majors and he still looks on him like a son, although he isn't all that much older. And maybe—yes, definitely, Len Carter. He's right fielder for the Boomers—he and Henry Grasso alternate, depending on whether a lefty or a righty pitches—and he really hates the Bandits, all of them, not just Prager, but Prager most of all. When he played for the Bandits they sent him down to the minors—Prager just took a dislike to him—and it took him four years to come back up again. He's a little wild, a very angry young man. That's it, Danzig, the ones with the biggest grudges."

"How come you didn't mention Warren Lamburt, Burr? You a friend of his or something?"

"Me? Not especially. I mean, everybody likes him, but he's not particularly—"

"Doesn't he hate Prager?"

"Well, sure. Everybody—Yes, I guess he does. When he signed with the Bandits, his agent—Lamburt was very hot then, one of the all-time greats—forced a very tough contract on Prager. Prager doesn't like to be beaten at anything, so he—whenever he had a press conference—he put the knife into Lamburt. Deep. Very nasty. Personal stuff. Very personal. That kind of thing."

"Lamburt's a good pitcher, isn't he? Famous for his good control?"

"You really think . . . ? Not Warren. He's not the type."

"Everybody's not the type, Burr, until they do it. You realize every one of these guys you mentioned, Bello, Sullivan, Blondin, Carter, Zarik, Lamburt, they're all ballplayers? With good arms? And motives? Who were on or near the field, or near Bello's office, when Prager was killed? Motive, means, and opportunity. And you

94

told me you didn't know who killed Prager?" Danzig stood up to go.

"Wait. I still don't. That's six of them. And you were going to tell me when Prager was killed."

Danzig hesitated for a moment, then said, "Around twelve-thirty, give or take a half hour. Now you got everything I know, just about. So let's figure out which one it is, Burr. Nothing to it. And let's do it fast; I got lots of other cases." He turned to go, then turned back. "Call me regular, let me know what you find out. And leave a big tip for the waitress; you held the table a long time, trying to con me you didn't know who done it."

The Gruber Dome was an ant's nest of activity when Marc got there, even though the start of the first game of the World Series was some time away. The Boomers, looking sleek and confident in their black-trimmed white uniforms, were completing their full field practice. Marc loved the atmosphere, the sight and the sound of the ball field, the crack of the bat, the thunk of the ball as it was caught, the cries of the coaches and the players, the smooth, easy, graceful movements of fielders and the relaxed throws of the pitchers warming up, the chatter and the good-natured insults of the playful athletes contrasting with the intense passion of the fans, who were already beginning to fill the stands.

The Gruber Dome was, technically, the most modern and efficient enclosed stadium in the world. Designed basically as a football and baseball stadium, its movable stands and versatile playing surface made it possible to convert from one sport to another in twenty-four hours and, in its short history, the Dome had already been used for soccer, hockey, basketball, tennis, wrestling, karate, and a world championship heavyweight boxing match.

The Brooklyn fans, on the home-team side of the stadium, were carrying the traditional gray-and-green rolled-up banners, which, predictably, would proclaim to the world, and to the TV cameras, that Brooklyn was the garden spot of the universe, that the Bandits would sweep the Series in four games or less, that Butch Bello was a genius, that John Carlson was the greatest, that Mario Demarco was the cutest, and that New Jersey was the dumps and the Boomers shouldn't even be allowed to come to Brooklyn without a passport. The Boomers' partisans, on the third-base side of the field, fewer in number but just as loud, their banners matching the black-and-white of their champions, and their opinions of Brooklyn and the Bandits, though not quite as offensive or as freely expressed as their hosts' uninhibited descriptions of the Boomers—they did, after all, have to get out of Brooklyn alive, but wait till we get them in Hague Stadium—left no doubt as to their contempt for anyone who was so stupid as to live in Brooklyn voluntarily.

Here and there a player was signing balls and cards for young fans, for very young fans, and for not-so-young fans, nonchalantly ignoring the rule, as they all did, which prohibited players in uniform from mingling with the spectators. Here and there, a few spectators were already on their third beers and would barely be able to see the field by the time the game started, and here and there arguments had already broken out about who didn't know shit about what if he thought that . . . The lights inside the Dome were not as bright as the sun nor as warm, the artificial turf was not as soft as real grass, nor did it smell as sweet, the air did not move as naturally nor feel as live as in an outdoor stadium, but Marc loved it, reveled in it, closed his eyes and felt happy in it. It was baseball, and that was enough.

It was ten three-ring circuses combined in one; wherever you looked there was something wonderful. Acrobatics, strength, speed, balance, coordination, team play, pressure, power, pride, planning, strategy, tactics, feinting, faking, spur-of-the-moment decisions, abilities stretching beyond the human to perform the impossible, and luck—definitely luck—all in the spotlight, no place to hide, each player playing his part, each with a chance to become a hero or a bum. Everything a game should have, could have, baseball had. Has. Always will have. Always.

This was really why he had become a sports reporter, and stayed a sports reporter, in spite of all his problems. It was the game that counted, that really counted. The game. In spite of all the hype, the creeps and the phonies, the Witters and the Pragers—above it all stood the game, baseball. The crowd too, and the players and the reporters and the TV cameramen—they didn't give a damn, today, about the perfidy of the U.N. or the malice of the IRS or the stupidity of the legislators or the murder of Slippery Sam Prager; they were all there to see the final test, the matching of champion against champion, David against Goliath, Bandits against Boomers, the World Series, the games that shook the world every fall—or America, at least, and the hearts of every red-blooded American boy who had ever fantasized hitting a homer with the bases full in the last of the ninth or dreamed of striking out Babe Ruth to win the Series.

Marc had to get some stories, but the few players in either color uniform who were not busy were already surrounded by notebooks and cameras. Marc, or any experienced reporter, could have written those stories in his sleep. The only reason for asking questions now was the hope of provoking a player or coach into making some thoughtless or angry remark that could lead to a feud or a headline. For that, Marc would talk to Len Carter. But later. Maybe after the game, especially if Carter got into the game and made an error. Or was struck out by a Bandit pitcher. Or was looked at cross-eyed by a Bandit coach. Or insulted by a Bandit fan. Or if the sun was shining. Or just asked if he would attend Sam Prager's funeral.

Sam Prager. That was the problem. Because of Harvey Danzig. A terrific combination. Danzig and Prager. With Marc caught in the middle. A thick sandwich. With capers on the side. Just because he wanted to . . . A truly noble motive. For Dahliah. And Danzig wanted an answer fast. Sure, Harvey, whatever you say. One fast solution coming right up. When did Danzig want it? Fast? How fast is fast? Danzig didn't say. Typical. That way, he could scream no matter how quickly Marc found out . . . What was he thinking about? How could he find out who . . . ? Maybe if he picked up enough information—Danzig was right about one thing: The suspects would talk to Marc more easily than to the police—he could keep Danzig from throwing him to the wolves. The other wolves. For a while. Then again, maybe something else would happen.

Like in the old joke. The king condemned the man to death. "Wait," the man begged. "If in only one year I teach your favorite horse to talk, will you let me leave the country alive?" The king, intrigued, agreed, but promised death by horrible torture if his horse did not learn to talk in one year. When the man's friend asked why he had made such a ridiculous offer, the man replied, "In one year, the king may die. Or the horse may die. Or I may die. Or the horse might even learn to talk."

Sure. Or Marc might find the killer. Fast. So might as well start now. Not with one of the players. Or coaches. Or managers. No way to get anything worthwhile from one of them; all they had on their minds now was the game.

"Didn't you pick up your press kit yesterday?" George Blondin asked. "I have plenty more." He started to get up from his desk, but Marc shook his head.

"I have all I need about the Bandits and how marvelous they are. I just dropped in to congratulate you about how well you killed all the speculation and gossip about the murder. For an ex-player, you've turned into a real pro."

"I'm going to take that as a compliment," Blondin said, smiling ruefully, "though from anyone but you . . ." The big plump man leaned back in his executive chair. "Most reporters think a PR guy is an unnecessary evil, a fast-talking con man who stands between them and the real honest truth. I'm proud of what I do, Marc, most of the time, and I'm pretty good at it too. I did go to college, you know, and I did get an M.A. in journalism. Maybe if I'd gone into the minors right out of high school, I'd have made it bigger as a player and I wouldn't have to be working for a living now. But that's the breaks."

"Actually, George, I wanted to pick your brain about the murder, and I figured you wouldn't be busy now."

"That's what I'm here for, to do all the research and the horse work and to put it in order so you reporters won't have to strain yourselves—but what makes you think I'm not busy? I have the funeral to take care of, the eulogies from all the dignitaries—you think their secretaries are going to dig up—and find—all the good things their bosses are going to have to say about the late deceased? And the players and coaches? The managers? The politicians? The *other* owners? They all hated him and it's up to me to make sure it's a good funeral. I just hope they can read the words without laughing. With some of the politicians, I just hope they can read."

"Why you? Aren't there any relatives? What about the association of Prager's ex-wives?"

"No relatives, no children that I know of, and all three ex-wives are busy getting fitted with sexy black widow's weeds. So who else is going to do it? His latest tootsie?"

"No heirs? What's going to happen to the team? The franchise?"

"Ask the executor, whoever that is. It's a corporation, so my guess is that everything will keep on going the same as before. Better. Westfield will keep on running the business end and, thank God, he doesn't have any interest in running the team on the field. Which means that we might have a chance to win a couple of games from the Boomers. When they liquidate the assets, the corporate stock will eventually be sold to a consortium of playboys. Serious lovers of the game don't have that kind of money."

"How will that affect you?"

"Could only be for the better; Sam was not a prince to work for, as you well know." Blondin blushed at the memory of the latest humiliation Marc had witnessed.

"You wanted him dead?" Marc asked bluntly.

"A thousand times," Blondin answered, equally bluntly. "As who didn't? And that's not for publication either, or don't I have to tell you that?"

"How will Prager's death affect the team? The Series?"

"The team has suffered a great loss, but they will try to win one today in memory of their beloved chief. Mr. Prager would have wanted it that way."

"Come on, George."

"Come on what? What the hell do you expect me to say for publication? That he was the most hated guy in baseball? Bar none?

That the guys who hated him most were the ones who he screwed the most—his own team? That the team will play better without him around bad-mouthing every little thing and never saying a good word about anybody? Screwing up the team with his stupid strategy? You know as well as I do that Prager's death was a blessing. To baseball and to the world." Blondin stopped for breath, his neck swollen, a vein distended, throbbing on his temple.

"I'm going to write a story." Marc said decisively. Definitely. It had come down to that; he knew it in his bones. The last time, he had tried to conceal his playing detective, and it had almost ended in his death. This time he would tell everyone, forthrightly, what he was doing. He couldn't end up any worse and it might shorten the time he would spend wondering when he would be killed and by whom. "A story every day. About the murder. I'm going to be an investigative reporter. In sports. Crime related to sports."

"Watch what you say, Marc." The big man looked very angry. Marc moved back. Though Blondin was overweight, Marc knew the ex-third baseman's strength and speed of reaction were still much greater than any ordinary man's. "I'm not kidding. I don't want anything I told you about Prager or the murder to be quoted. I'll deny it if you do and cut you off from any interviews with anybody on the team forever."

"Come on, George, we've worked together for five years; you know I wouldn't do that. I'll quote unnamed sources and write in generalities. But I do want to break this story. Actually, I have to. Both my boss and the police are on my neck. Don't forget, I found the body."

"So did Butch; that doesn't mean anything."

"To Lieutenant Danzig it does. He questioned me about Bello at length and now he's treating me like a suspect."

"He suspects Butch? He's crazy. Butch wouldn't . . . what did you tell him about . . . ? I don't want Butch bothered right now. By anything."

"Danzig suspects everybody, but I didn't tell him anything new

101

about Bello, just what everybody knows. Why? Do you think I would do anything to hurt . . . ? With the police?''

"If you thought he did it, sure you would. You're one of those types who'd . . . you're a reporter; you'd crucify your best friend if it would make a good headline.''

"Not crucify—report the facts. If he was a murderer, that is. What's wrong with that, George? If I knew who the killer was, why shouldn't I publish it? Wouldn't you?''

"Hell no, not in this case. I'd give him a medal and take up a collection to help him get to Rio.''

"A murderer?''

"The guy who did this . . . Prager killed lots of people in his day. Maybe not directly, but he did it just as sure as if he used a gun. Ask anybody who ever had the slightest contact with him. You think what he did—used to do to me—was bad? Hell, I'm still eating. There are people, good people, who . . . The guy who beaned Prager was not a murderer; he was doing a job that had to be done for the benefit of humanity. An exterminator.'' Blondin's face was flushed. "Why are you asking me about it?''

"Because you're a suspect too, George. If Danzig hasn't gotten to you yet, don't worry, he will. Everyone who was in the ballpark at the time Danzig was killed is a suspect.''

"Lots of luck to him, then; there must've been two hundred people there.''

"But not all of them had your opportunity and your motive. And your arm.''

"I'm not a pitcher.''

"The throw from third to first is more than twice the pitching distance. Your arm has to be stronger than any pitcher's.''

"What about control? When I was playing, all I had to do was put it inside a fifteen-foot circle and the first baseman would get it. Even on a bounce. And that's when I was playing.''

"Prager was hit from no more than thirty feet away. A high-school kid could have done it. A breeze for anyone who ever played in the majors.''

102

"What the hell are you doing, Marc? Accusing me?"

Marc attacked. "How long would it have taken you to walk from here to Butch's tunnel? Five minutes?"

"I wasn't inside; I was on the field most of the time, making sure the reporters and photographers, the cameramen, they were all happy."

"You were seen in right field about the time Prager was killed." A shot in the dark. "Right outside the last tunnel."

"I was seen all over, so what?" The shot had struck home.

"Picking up a ball?"

"A ball comes near me, it's only natural. But I threw them all back."

"No way to prove that, is there?"

"Why the hell do I have to prove anything? The police—they have to prove I did it. And they can't. I didn't, that's all there is to it. And what the hell gives you the right to ask me these questions."

"I can ask you anything I want, George. You don't have to answer, but it might be better for you if you do. What I ask you, the police will ask twice as hard. And be twice as hard to satisfy, so look at this as a sort of rehearsal. If I believe you, I'm going to write my story from a very sympathetic viewpoint, which might help to take some of the pressure off you. If I don't believe you, well, you said it yourself, I'm one of those types who'd turn in his own mother for a story."

"You don't have to believe me, Marc. Just use your head. Why would I want to kill . . . ? All right, 'want to' is one thing, but doing it is another. I stood him for five years, I could have stood him for another ten. More. Every time he gave me some shit, sure I'd get mad, but then I'd think of what I have at home, what I'm working for, and you know what, Marc? With all his money, with all his power, I'm richer than he is. He'll never have what I have, and what's more, he *couldn't* have it. Wouldn't know it if it fell right in his lap. So why should I risk all that, my home, my family, just to get another boss? Who might even not renew my contract, especially if he had a brother-in-law who thought he could do what I do as good as I do it, even half as good. Or might try to force me out right now, even if I kissed his ass good. At least with Prager, I knew if I took his shit, I'd be here forever. So you better believe I didn't do it.''

"Well, that sounds reasonable, but it doesn't explain why your fingerprints are on the ball that killed Prager.'' Another shot in the dark, but no way Blondin could know that. Marc would have to ask Danzig—should have thought of that before.

"Are you kidding, Marc? There must be a hundred fingerprints on that ball. If it was used in practice, everybody touched it. Including me. Doesn't mean a thing.''

"Did you see anything? Anyone near that tunnel? Anyone throwing a ball into the tunnel? At the time Prager was killed?''

"When was that?''

"Between twelve and one, more or less.''

"There must've been a dozen people around there, maybe even more, around that time, but I didn't see anyone doing anything like that. 'Course, I wasn't there all the time, or looking that way or particularly paying attention, but I didn't see anything suspicious.''

"And you wouldn't tell me if you had, would you?'' Marc stood up. "OK, George, I'll talk to you again. I've got to go out and interview some of the other suspects.''

"What you said before, the story you're going to write. I leveled with you, Marc, all the way. Honest. I want you to make the story favorable, how cooperative I was. How professional. And that I'm not a suspect. Don't even mention that the police are even considering me a suspect. Like where I was at the time and the fingerprints and all that. Just don't bring it up, OK?''

"Sure, but what are you worried about? The police don't use my stories for evidence.''

"Not the police—the new owner, whoever he is. He might not like it if he thought I'd been on a list of suspects for killing the owner of the Bandits.''

"Yeah, there is that. OK, George, I'll play it down, make it all

104

anonymous sources and mention no names. See you after the game."

"That's another thing, Marc. Don't interview any more suspects now. It's getting close to game time, and everybody's nervous. I don't want to take any chances on blowing the game. It's the first game of the Series, and it's very important, psychologically, to win it."

Marc was astonished. "You think the Bandits have a chance against the Boomers? With their hitting, and both your best pitchers tired . . . ? Forget it."

"There's something you forgot. Prager is dead. He isn't going to interfere with the team anymore. Butch can manage his best and the team can play its best."

"You got money on the game? Off the record."

Blondin hesitated, then said, "I found a guy—he's giving eleven to five. At those odds, it's crazy not to bet. For a short series? Hell, in my day, I've seen lots of sure things that didn't end up the way everybody figured they had to. You may be in for a big surprise. We're a good team, Marc, don't you forget it. The Boomers may be in for a surprise too."

"OK, I won't talk to anybody till after the game." Marc walked to the door of the office.

As Marc opened the door, Blondin said, "I don't mind if you talk to any of the Boomers. Some of them hated Prager worse than any of the Bandits did. And I don't mind if you shake them up. Every little bit helps."

"You really want to win, don't you?"

"Damn right. We all do. In spite of Prager, it's my team. Our team."

Marc closed the door softly behind him. Another motive. Maybe the primary motive. Not just for George Blondin, but for everybody. Like little boys—in a sense, all ballplayers were little boys; otherwise why would someone like Warren Lamburt keep knocking his brains out in the hot sun at forty, and feel worried, lost, if he couldn't play baseball—our team must win. Must. The owner might treat you like shit, but it's still our team. The manager might be a bastard, but it's still our team. The fans might be animals and you might live three thousand miles away, but it's still our team. Your teammates might be monsters, but it's our team. *Our* team. And for the team, to win, for the *team,* you could do anything, *would* do anything, even things you wouldn't do for yourself. Anything. Including murder.

15

Enzo Bello, manager of the National League Champions, the Brooklyn Bandits, and Daniel Zarik, manager of the American League Champions, the Jersey Boomers, walked slowly and formally up to Charles Hunneker, the head umpire. Bello handed him two copies of his batting order, then Zarik handed in two of his. Hunneker carefully checked each set to make sure they were true duplicates, handed each manager one copy of the opposing team's batting order, and put the other copies into his inside pocket.

Bello glanced at the Boomers' batting order and jerked his head up in surprise. "You gone crazy, Dan? Just to get all righty hitters? And the sluggers up front?"

"Me?" Zarik's death's-head face was white with rage. "What about you? Starting Lamburt? When anyone with a bit of sense would have gone to Muldoon or Padilla?"

"Yeah, I figured that would shake you up a bit."

"Not half as much as it'll shake you up when my boys tee off on his half-assed fastball. I hope you got plenty of balls in stock; the kids in left-field bleachers are going to get a lot of them for autographs."

"May I remind you *gentlemen*," Hunneker said sarcastically, "that rule three-point-oh-nine does not permit opposing teams to fraternize while in uniform."

"If you call this fraternizing, Hunk," Butch said, "I'd hate to see how you call balls and strikes."

"I calls 'em as I sees 'em," Hunneker said quietly. "Unless I'm so upset I can't see straight. You wouldn't want, either of you *gentlemen,* to upset me that much, would you?"

Butch and Dan had sense enough to keep their mouths shut. "No? Good. Then—*play ball,*" he shouted.

"Take a look at this." In the dugout Bello showed the Boomers' batting order to Corey Steen, who would be starting catcher until Krumanski's finger healed.

Steen glanced at the sheet, then took it out of Butch's hand. "He's gone off his rocker."

"That ain't the point," Verne Sullivan said. "Have you figured out what to call for?"

"Don't worry, Verne. I got the book on every hitter in both leagues in my head."

"Low and inside," Verne insisted. "Curves, sliders, and sinkers, that's all I want to see. No fastballs in the strike zone; that left-field fence is too damn close. In fact, no straight fastballs at all. Lamburt don't have the speed no more."

"Keep the outfield bunched left," Earl Diggins said, "and playing deep. The infield too—shift them six, seven feet over and ten feet further back. They got seven righties in the lineup, all long-ball hitters."

"Len Carter don't have that much power."

"Brush him back once," Sullivan said. "He loses his cool easy."

"Yeah?" Steen was skeptical. "What if he rushes Lamburt?"

"You gotta stop him. Lamburt's the only righty starter we got. Catch him."

"Wearing all my protection? You got to be kidding. Tell Johnson to come over from first."

"So Carter kills our best hitter?" Butch interjected. "Then Carter gets thrown out of the game, Zarik puts in Grasso, and we put in who instead of Johnson? I can afford to lose an outfielder; I can't lose my first baseman. No, that's why that bastard Zarik—that's the sonofabitch who tried to take over my job—put in Carter in the first

108

place, to start a fight and cripple one of our best men and get thrown out. I don't want no brushbacks on Carter, you hear, Corey? And no beanballs on anyone, even with Carter on the bench; he's awful fast coming out of the dugout and he's replaceable—our boys ain't. If an accident happens, let Lamburt take care of himself; he's big enough. Throw the ball back to him fast. With his control, he can clip Carter right on the nose before he gets halfway to the mound.

Warren Lamburt threw his first warm-up pitch. It moved slowly through the air, about 70 percent speed, wavered a little when it came to the plate, and dived down and to the left. Corey Steen barely smothered the ball on the ground with his mitt. Angrily, he picked up the ball in his bare right hand and stalked out to the pitcher's mound. "What the hell you trying to do?" he demanded. "Verne said you had to use your good hard stuff, low and inside. Didn't you warm up enough before?"

"I'm going to pitch knuckleballs today, Corey," Warren explained. "These guys'll kill me if I try to pitch regular. They're swinging for the fences. We'll lose the game for sure. This way we got a chance."

"I can't hold a knuckler half the time. You already split Krumanski's finger. If you don't know where the ball's going, how the hell can I? I'm telling Butch to take you out of the game right now."

"He can't. The rules say I got to pitch to at least one batter until he's out or gets on base." Lamburt looked at Steen's sullen face. "Look, Corey, don't worry about catching every ball; just stop them. I'll keep them low, so there won't be any passed balls charged against you."

"You gonna start finding control now? In eight warm-up pitches? Who you kidding?"

"I've been practicing at home, at a target. Look, see how I do against Battles. If you think I can't find the plate, or if he gets a solid hit, I'll throw whatever you want."

Without a word, Steen strode back to the plate.

*   *   *

"Did you see what that sonofabitch Bello did?" Dan Zarik raged. "One of us opened his mouth, that's what and Butch *knew* I was going to play all righties. That's why he put in Lamburt to start."

"Take it easy, Dan." Batting coach Rich Martini was talking calmly and soothingly. "The only ones who knew was you and me, and that was only yesterday. What he did, we should've guessed. He's figuring this game is lost anyway, so he'll give another day's rest to Carlson and Androvec. Padilla and Muldoon too. Lamburt don't have the speed anymore, so let's just relax and start with a win. Big hits, like you said. The way you figured originally."

"Look at that." Irv Nessen, the pitching coach, was excited. "Lamburt's throwing knuckleballs."

"That's good," Martini said. "He hasn't thrown a dozen knucklers this season yet. We'll use him for batting practice." He waved Sam Battles over. "I want you to take the first two balls, no matter how good they look. Let's see if Lamburt can find the plate. After that, if it comes in the strike zone, knock it outta here. This game, we don't want just hits, we want homers. Early on. Get a full three inches closer to the plate and right up to the front end of the batter's box, so you can catch the ball before it breaks all the way. And swing for below the ball, got that? *Below*—that's the way to hit a knuckler. And remember, it's coming a lot slower. Maybe use a bat an ounce heavier?"

Battles nodded grimly, selected a bat, and walked slowly out of the dugout. He put a lead doughnut on the bat and took a few practice swings to loosen up. Right fielder Len Carter followed him out and knelt in the on-deck circle.

Warren Lamburt wound up and threw the first ball. It moved slowly and hazily across the plate, just at Battles's knees. "Strike," the umpire called. The second pitch weaved a little, then cut across a corner of the plate, a second strike. Battles stepped out of the batter's box, tightened his batting gloves, and went back in again. The third pitch was coming in perfectly, waist high, right over the center of the plate. Battles shifted his weight, took a hard cut, and missed the ball by a full foot. Scowling, he walked back to the Boomers' dugout. "Below," Rich Martini whispered. "I told you swing below."

"How the hell can you swing below a ball that hits the plate?" Sam Battles asked of no one in particular.

Len Carter moved into the batter's box, choking his bat slightly. Warren Lamburt looked at Corey Steen. In or out? Steen impatiently waved him to quit stalling and start pitching. Lamburt's first pitch was an easy strike, right across the center of the plate, with nothing on it, but Carter had already decided not to swing. The second pitch looked the same. Carter took a good cut and fouled off the ball. The third pitch was a ball. On the fourth pitch, Carter took a shortened swing and topped the ball, an easy grounder to third. Alvin Smootra took one step and threw him out to Reuben Johnson at first. Two down.

Center fielder Jason Cordray, one of the Boomers' most dangerous hitters, was up third. He went down swinging on three consecutive pitches, then threw his bat away in disgust.

There was applause for Warren Lamburt as he left the field. Verne Sullivan met him as he entered the dugout. "I don't like guys who don't follow orders," he told Lamburt.

"I want to win this game as much as you, Verne," the pitcher said. "I wasn't trying to show you up."

"Depending how you do," Bello said, "I'm either gonna fine you five thousand or kiss you."

"If I've got the choice," Lamburt said, smiling for the first time that day, "I'll pay the five thousand."

The Bandits' second baseman, Joe Kullman, lined out to center. Alvin Smootra hit a weak single off Greg Harriman, just out of reach of Art Casey at first, and stole second on the next pitch. Left fielder Bob Coffee fouled off three pitches before he finally walked, putting men on first and second, and bringing up Mario Demarco, the handsome right fielder.

On a count of two-and-two, Demarco hit a fly deep to the

right-field corner. Smootra tagged up, and when Len Carter caught the ball over his shoulder, took off. Boomer shortstop Emilio Leon cut the ball off in an attempt to get the runner at second, but Coffee had gone back to first, so Leon hurriedly threw to Battles at third. Smootra, three steps toward home, dived back fast, and both runners were safe. It was men on first and third, with two out and Reuben Johnson, the best hitter on the Bandits, at bat.

Harriman's first pitch was a low fastball. Johnson cut at the pitch viciously, spinning around and barely staying erect, clearly trying to put one over the right-field fence. As Harriman went into his next pitch, Smootra took off at top speed from third. The pitch was low and inside, and Johnson, the slowest man on the team, bunted clumsily between first and pitcher, to the total surprise of all the Boomers. Casey and the shocked Harriman raced for the ball, ignoring Johnson. Harriman got there first and, flustered, snapped the ball to the catcher, Hedstrom, just as Smootra slid into the plate. Hedstrom dived for Smootra, but the umpire's hands were flat out. Safe! The first run of the series had been scored by the Bandits!

The Brooklyn crowd stood up and screamed, as only a Brooklyn crowd can, waving banners and thrusting fists into the air. In the dugout, Alvin Smootra was slapping hands happily as Sullivan and Diggins were congratulating Butch Bello on the success of his strategy. "It worked," Bello said, glowing. "We did it. That Johnson. First time in his life he ever bunted safe."

"Yeah," Sullivan said, "but you took a big chance telling him to fake on the first swing and bunt on the second pitch. Suppose Harriman had thrown him a high one. We could have had a pop-up or an easy high fly. Then you would have been a bum. Or if Harriman had been in a position to throw Johnson out at first, it would have been three gone and no score."

"Sometimes you got to take a chance. With Johnson, everybody was laying back, looking for him to try to put one out of the park. I figured Harriman pitching Johnson low inside to prevent a homer and on the shock to make them all look to get Smootra at the plate instead of Johnson at first, especially since Harriman's a righty and could see Smootra taking off from third. Also, the bunt was to Harriman's left, so he picked it up in his glove and had to transfer it to his right hand to throw, which gave us another half a second for Smootra to score. Using Johnson to bunt was also a surprise to them."

"You're a tricky bastard, Butch," Sullivan said, "but these complicated plays can blow up in your face. Don't pull too many more of those surprises—I almost swallowed my chaw."

Corey Steen came up with two out and men on first and second. Harriman bore down and, with the count two-and-nothing, Steen hit a hard line drive directly to Battles at third, and the side was retired.

The next three innings were a pitchers' duel, both Lamburt and Harriman giving up an occasional hit or walk, with neither team able to get a man past second base. Finally, in the beginning of the fifth, Art Casey connected with a Lamburt knuckleball that spun enough to give it a slow, predictable curve and parked it high in the right-field stands for a home run, tying the score. The Jersey side of the stands cheered, but it was a muted joy, with the realization that the Brooklyn team would not be the walkover they had envisioned.

In the Bandits' half of that inning, the top of the batting order came around again. Joe Kullman ripped a hard grounder past the pitcher that Leon could not get to, bringing up Smootra. Casey stayed close to the bag, ready for a pickoff, but Kullman took a long lead off first, ready for a steal or an overthrow. Harriman threw to first twice, but each time Kullman got back in time. Carter, the right fielder, was pulled in tight to protect against a Texas Leaguer. Harriman's first pitch was slightly high and Smootra missed a hard swing at a slider. On the third pitch, Kullman took off and Smootra popped one past third, just over Battles's head.

With none out and men on first and third, Coffee came up, looking grim. He swung hard at the first ball as Smootra stole second without a play by the catcher. The next two pitches were balls, the second almost hitting Coffee in the knee. The third pitch was a slider that Coffee fouled off to make it two-and-two. Coffee fouled off three consecutive pitches, one of them going into the left-field stands, foul by inches. He hit the next pitch, a hard one-hop smash directly to the shortstop. Leon faked Kullman back to third and whipped a throw to Casey at first, getting Coffee out by two steps.

The Brooklyn stands went crazy again as the clean-up hitter, Demarco, came to bat with one out and two men on, the screams of the teenage girls in the bleachers adding a note of hysterical frenzy to the bedlam. Demarco let a called strike and two balls go by before he connected perfectly on a slow curve. Running toward first, he watched intently as the ball arched toward the right center-field fence, with Len Carter running desperately, back turned, to where the ball would go over. At the perfect moment, Carter ran up the wall, caught the ball just over the top, and fell heavily to the ground. Immediately he raised his gloved hand, then flipped the ball to center fielder Jason Cordray, who had run over to help. Cordray threw the ball to Mel Wheatley at second, who faked a throw to home and snapped it to Battles, to hold Smootra at third. The Jersey fans cheered Carter while the Brooklyn fans booed. Two out, but Kullman had scored easily.

Powerful Reuben Johnson came to bat with a man on third. Harriman gave Johnson an intentional base on balls to get at Corey Steen, a somewhat weaker hitter, and to set up a force play at second for the slow-moving Johnson. Steen hit the second pitch for what would have been a sure hit, forcing the shortstop deep into the hole, but Leon whipped the ball to Wheatley to beat Johnson to second by a step. Third out, and the Bandits were leading by a score of 2–1.

The next three innings saw no scoring, although in the top of the seventh, the Boomers left two men on base as Lamburt struck out the last two men in a row. In the top of the ninth, Dan Zarik pulled the weak-hitting leadoff man, Emilio Leon, for the erratic, left-handed Henry Grasso, who nervously pumped a bad pitch into left field for a single. Harriman was still pitching strongly and had given up only two runs, but this was their last chance, so Zarik called in Hale Porter, another left-handed outfielder, to pinch-hit.

114

Lamburt, realizing the tension of the pinch hitter, tried to get the ball over the center of the plate, waist high, to make it as tempting to swing at as possible, fighting all his experience as a pitcher to barely clip the corners and never to give a powerful hitter a good ball to swing at. But the idea of the knuckleball is to make it look so easy to hit that even the most careful batter will swing. And miss, as the ball ducks away and down from anyplace it might possibly have been expected to go. So when the batter is under great stress, anxious, you offer him a perfect home-run ball that he can't possibly miss. And he misses. Porter went down in three. One out.

Sam Battles was up next. He took one strike, swung at a second, and topped the third pitch to send a slow grounder to Pancho Rivera at short. Rivera flipped the ball to Joe Kullman, who jumped to avoid Grasso's slide, and threw to Johnson for the double play that ended the game. The Bandits had won!

The Brooklyn fans went even crazier than before, yelling and cheering, jumping onto the field to hug their heroes, to kiss them, to offer them Canarsie and points east plus half their kingdoms and their daughters' hands in marriage. The players ran for the locker room and the reporters ran for the telephones, plugged in their modems, and frantically typed the lead and final paragraphs of their stories. As soon as the stories were sent, the reporters dashed for the elevator that would take them down to the locker-room level, down to where they could get the human-interest stories and share the festivities and the jubilation and the feeling of our side having won. Some of the older, wiser reporters made their way to the Boomers' locker room, for the more poignant tales of the death of kings, the sagas of kings dethroned, and the promises of vengeance on the morrow.

Marc slowly finished typing his story of the game and sat staring at the terminal. No one on either side of the field would want to talk about the murder of Samuel Moultran Prager now, nor be able to tell the truth if he did. No Bandit with beer in his hair would want his spirits dampened or his cheek made pale with care just because his owner—an *owner*—had been murdered. No Boomer wearing white sackcloth trimmed with black ashes could bring himself to spare the smallest tear over the all-too-timely death of the man who bought the team that killed the dream of their invincibility, the promise of their immortality. No one would want to be reminded that, sooner or later, in baseball as in the Real Game, we die, we all die.

Let the others repeat the stories that the fans annually forgot, of the joys of victory and the pains of defeat, as told by the not-very-literate but often poetic great players of the world. Marc would write about Sam Prager, who had accomplished in death what he had never achieved in life: an honest victory.

16

"I didn't expect you home this early," Dahliah said. "Doesn't Mr. Witter need you for something? Sharpening pencils? Licking boots? *Anything?*"

"Don't, Dahliah." Marc plopped down wearily on the couch in the living-room area. "Please. I had a hard day today."

"Watching the big boys play ball? Gee, that must have taken a lot out of you. Unfortunately, I already ate. Maybe you can find something left over in the rat trap?"

"I ate out. I didn't want to trouble you."

"Good to be rich, isn't it? I wish I could afford to be served by groveling waiters."

"Come on, Dahliah, a hot dog, a knish, and a Coke? Off a wagon?"

"You ate *what*?" She choked.

"It was late and I was starving and it was the only—"

"Oh, my God." She put her hands to her face. "You're trying to commit suicide. Just because I . . . ." She rushed to his side, knelt on the floor, and put her arms around him. "I didn't want you to die, darling. All I wanted was for you to remember our first anniversary. That's all. And to be on time. To be on time and bring a few flowers. A few flowers and maybe a small gift as a memento. Something that I could wear to make my colleagues at school envious and show them what a nice lover I have. I don't want you to even think of killing yourself just to impress me. And in such a horrible way. Meat. Preservatives. Super-saturated fats. Caffeine. *Sugar.*"

Marc looked at her suspiciously, but she was not smiling. He decided to test the waters. "OK, I won't. For now. But the next time you banish me, I'm going to eat a whole steak. Rare. Aged. With French fries. And ketchup." Still no smile. He was safe. He put his arms around her. "There, isn't that better than fighting?" He kissed Dahliah hungrily.

She drew away. "I can't. You smell of dead animals. Meat. I can't love a man who has death all over him. You'll have to take a lot of showers before it wears off."

"OK, I'll take a hot shower right now. Wait for me." He stared toward the bathroom.

She stopped him. "I forgot to tell you. Witter called. He said to call him as soon as you came in. At the office." She watched him carefully.

Marc hesitated, then, "Might as well get it over with," he said overcasually.

The editor answered on the second ring. "You have a lead?" he asked. "A good lead?"

"Not yet, I'm still laying the groundwork, but Danzig wants results fast, so I'm sure to have something to print soon."

"You're stalling, Burr, I can tell, but if you want the opportunity to fall flat on your face, I'll gladly give it to you. Don't forget I want you in the office tomorrow morning to edit Nelda Shaver's page. It goes every Monday, in case you hadn't noticed, with the rest of the Sports Special."

"This is Saturday night, Julius, in case you hadn't noticed, and I don't work Saturday nights. Especially this weekend, which is Dahliah's—our—anniversary. I've just put in a full day's work on the first game of the Series as well as getting the story of the Prager murder. Which I have to work on tomorrow too, at least two interviews, if I'm to have any chance of getting the information I need before Christmas, plus my regular stories of the second game and my Monday column. So I'm not coming in tomorrow either.

118

From now on, Nelda Shaver has to get her page in by Thursday close, so I can edit it on Friday. Which, knowing her, will mean rewriting every word. Figure a whole day's work, since I'll have to explain the two-syllable words to her, so keep in mind that I can't go out on a story then.''

"An excellent idea, Burr. I'll do you the favor of editing 'The Sporting Woman' page myself tomorrow, out of consideration for Dahliah, not for you. As for Nelda's getting her week's news in on Thursday, by all means tell her that. Just make sure she doesn't run to Mr. Heisenberg and insist that he horsewhip you before he fires you. If you're still employed after that, which would be extremely doubtful since Nelda is much better-looking than you are, you may wish to persuade the lady—I'm sure you know how *that* can be done—you can *try* persuade her to *beg* Lucy Stone Valentine, very politely, not to sue me, *The Sentry*, and you, in that order, for sexual harassment. Other than that, have a happy anniversary.''

Marc hung up slowly. Dahliah came over to him and hugged him closely. "I'm proud of you, darling. It's about time you told off that nasty old bully. He'll respect you more now, and I'll . . ." She kissed him slowly and warmly. Deeply. "Don't bother about the shower now. You can shower later. And get the paper tomorrow.''

The phone rang. Dahliah stopped kissing and just looked at him. Marc let it ring and ring, but it wouldn't stop. Just kept on ringing. When he couldn't resist anymore, he gently pulled one hand out of Dahliah's embrace and picked up the phone.

"Why the hell didn't you call me?" Lieutenant Danzig asked. "You're supposed to call me every day.''

"Yes, well . . ." Dahliah slowly and carefully moved his other arm from around her waist and distanced herself.

"Never mind that. What did you find out?''

"Not a thing. That is, I talked to George Blondin and got . . . he's a definite suspect, but I can't prove anything yet. I have to interrogate the others first before I can put the whole story together.''

119

"Only one? The whole day? What the hell's the matter with you, Burr—you trying to antagonize me?"

"The first game of the Series was being played. Nobody would have . . . it was impossible."

"Yeah? Well, we don't have that much time left. Meet me tomorrow, same time, same place. I got some things to discuss with you."

"Tomorrow? Sunday morning? It's my anniversary."

"Anniversary? The dame I met in the hospital? I thought it's *Miss* Norman. You get married without letting me know?"

"It's still Miss Norman, and it's still our anniversary."

"OK, if that's the way it is with you hippies, I'll move with the times." Marc could just visualize Danzig shaking his head at the sinfulness of the younger generation.

"I'll call you tomorrow, late. Meanwhile, I need some more information. Now. So I can ask the right questions. First, when did Prager get to the Dome? Where did he go in? And when? Did he have an appointment with anyone? Did he meet with anyone? What did he go there for? How did he get there? I need everything you know." Marc glanced sideways at Dahliah. She appeared deeply interested in what he was saying. Or at least she was listening.

"It ain't much," Danzig reported, "but I don't want it talked around. The chauffeur drove Prager there in his limo. He parked by the bunch of hydrants that the beat knows is reserved for the owner and his guests. The chauffeur don't know why he went there or anything; he just waited in the car. Took a nap, in fact, 'cause Prager never tells him how long he's gonna be. They got there about twelve noon, give or take a few minutes, the chauffeur ain't sure. Prager didn't mention any appointment and, as far as I know, he didn't see anybody. Prager went in by the private entrance that nobody can use but the big shots. No guard, so if one of the big shots wants to take his girlfriend up to the owner's box for a quickie, there ain't no witnesses."

"What private entrance? Where is it? I never knew there was a private entrance."

120

"You know that hall to the outside, just before you get to Bello's office?"

"The one near the owner's elevator? By the fire stair?"

"That's the one. Well, at the far end, to the right, is the private entrance. If you're outside, you can't open the fire door to get in. Besides, an alarm rings when the door is opened. So there's a door next to the fire door, with a good lock. Open that door and you're in a little vestibule, about six by three, at the other end of which is a door into the passage. Down the passage to the main corridor, turn right a couple of steps, and you're at the passage to Bello's office. Ten, twelve steps and you're right by the office."

"So Prager could have been going to drop in on Bello?"

"Could be. He liked to drop in on people unexpected. That's what he must've done; otherwise, why would his body be right at Bello's door?"

"Yes, but he was hit coming out, on the right side. Which means he had already been in Butch's office. Or, at least, the waiting room. That's usually not locked."

"He could have gone in the office too. I get the idea Prager had keys to everybody's office and their desks too. But I been thinking. Prager didn't have to be coming out when he was killed."

"Sure he did. He was hit on the right side, and the ball was on the field side of the tunnel."

"He could've been beaned going in, and when Prager spun around from being hit, the ball went off on the other side. Or the guy who threw it, he could have moved the ball on his way out of the tunnel."

More complications. Marc sighed. "Any fingerprints on the ball?"

"Millions, partials, some wiped out. It was a used ball, not a new one. No good for evidence. That's all I got, so far. Make sure you call me tomorrow." Danzig hung up.

Marc hung up too, slowly, and turned to Dahliah. She was sitting at the other end of the couch. "Finished?" she asked politely. Marc nodded. "Good. After you take your shower, you can get dressed and pick up the paper."

He looked at his watch. "But it won't be out for at least an hour."

"That's all right," Dahliah said.

17

"If you was Dan Zarik," Butch Bello asked, not taking his eyes off the practice on the field, "who would you figure me to start in this game with?"

"Dan played in the same league as me for twenty years," Verne Sullivan said, "and he knows how I think." Sullivan kept his eyes focused on Pedro Padilla, throwing easily to Corey Steen. "It gotta be Muldoon, and not just because he's had the most rest. It can't be Carlson. He needs at least two more days' rest, maybe more. The last game of the playoffs, we had to massage his arm the last three innings and, even then, we had to relieve him in the ninth. Androvec needs another day's rest too and I really want to give him two or three. That last month of the season took a lot out of everybody."

"So why not Padilla?"

"I'm figuring ahead, Butch. We're gonna lose today. No"—he waved off Bello's objections—"I'm not giving up in advance; I'm being practical. Zarik knows we got to use a lefty this game—we got nothing but lefty starters left; you can thank your friend Prager for that—so Dan's going to keep his same lineup as yesterday, just about, heavy on the right-handed hitters. Padilla's a stuff pitcher, a little better against righties than Muldoon and, what's worse, Muldoon is a fastballer. The Boomers will kill him. They're going to be real mad today, all hepped up, and they'll be zeroing in on whoever we put in, don't make no difference whether it's Padilla or Muldoon. So between the two, I'd rather save Padilla for later, when I got a chance to win. I'll bet you a big dinner, real Texas chili made by me, that we yank Muldoon by the fifth.''

"You writing this game off complete?"

"Not all the way; in baseball, you never know. But I'm figuring we lose today, Monday's a rest day, then I bring in Carlson for Tuesday. He'll be rested and we got a real good chance to win that one. OK, then Androvec for Game Four and we got a good chance to win that one. Let's say we don't win 'em both; we split and the score is two games each. On Thursday I start Lamburt and—"

"Lamburt? I thought you didn't like Lamburt."

"I didn't and I still don't, but facts is facts. He went a full nine innings and held the Boomers down to one run. With plenty of rest, he just might do it again. OK, if he does, now it's three to two, our favor. Then Friday's another rest day and Saturday I start Padilla. He'll be plenty rested, his stuff will be breaking sharp, and the Boomers'll be pressing. So we got a good chance to win the Series in six. But if Padilla loses, I still got Carlson on a five-day rotation for the seventh game."

"You know, Verne, a few days ago you wouldn't have bet a nickel on the Series going five games. Now you're talking like we could win."

"A couple of things happened since then," Sullivan protested. "Lamburt pitched a good game—all right, I give you credit for starting him—and you got away with some real tricky plays which, a tenth of a second wrong, you would have been a bum. I always said—even when you was a rookie catcher, remember?—don't worry about his looks, that kid got more smarts than the manager. And more balls. If we'da had a kid, Butch, I'da wanted him to be just like you."

"Yeah, I never forgot that," Bello said warmly, "and you know I feel the same about you. But you got to remember, we had a piece of good luck that . . . without it, I couldn't have done a thing, and we would've lost in four straight, for sure."

"Prager? Yeah, it might be a little—you know—calling that good luck but, hell, it's the truth. If he was around, we couldn't

124

have done a thing." He thought for a moment. "You got any ideas who done it?" he asked casually.

"I was sort of hoping it was you." Bello smiled crookedly. "I'd like to vote an extra World Series share to whoever it was; he deserves it. And I know the rest of the team would go along." He looked at Sullivan sharply. "You ain't thinking of helping that Danzig, are you?"

"It'll be a cold day in hell before . . . Whoever it was, God bless him," Sullivan said, "so even if I knew something, which I don't, I wouldn't give him away. Why're you asking me? You thinking it was one of the pitchers? My pitchers?"

"Well, when it comes to beanballs . . ."

"Put it out of your head, Butch. Right out. At that distance, anybody could've hit Prager hard enough. And accurate. Didn't have to be a pitcher. Besides, I need all my pitchers."

"You think it was done spur of the moment?"

"Had to be. Somebody near the tunnel had a ball in his hand, noticed Prager coming out of your office, and let go. One second and it's over. No risk. No thinking, even. Might not even have wanted to kill him, just do *something* to the bastard. To get even."

"Pretty dark in the tunnel, still . . . Might have gone that way. Even if he didn't kill Prager, even if he missed complete, Prager'd never know who it was."

"You got something else in mind, Butch, I don't want to hear it. The dark tunnel? Hell, anybody saw Prager, they'd know who he was at midnight. No way to mistake that runt for a ballplayer. And anybody around here who had the chance, if he was in the right mood, he'd've thrown that ball, including me and you. But don't go around thinking it had to be a Bandit. Plenty of Boomers got reason to hate Prager. Zarik, for one. And Carter too." There was silence for a moment, then Sullivan changed the subject. "You going to the funeral tomorrow?"

"Yeah. I got to. I even got to say something nice. What the hell, I've done worse in my life. You going?"

"Somebody gotta be there to stop you from calling the preacher a liar right out loud. Ain't I always stood by you?"

"Goes both ways, Verne. Now let's get on with the what-if. Suppose they get on Lamburt on Thursday and it's three games to two, their favor. Friday's off and Saturday's the crucial game. You still going to pitch Padilla in that game?"

"Hell no. Not that Padilla ain't good, but Carlson's my ace. He'll have close to four days' rest, and I'm gonna put him in if I gotta pack his whole body in ice between innings. Then if we win that one, I'll take my chances with Padilla for the last game, and at the first sign of trouble, I bring in my relievers and pray. My righties first, Sadoff and Ortiz, then Lengo, if I got to."

"So you figure today's game is gone?"

"That's the odds, but nothing's for sure. What you asked me was how Zarik would figure what I'd do. Well, that's how I'd really do it and that's how any manager in the league would do it too."

"That's how I'd do it too, normally, but maybe it's time to try something fancy."

"Another one of your ten-to-one shots, Butch? In the Series? We're ahead now; let's play it conservative. If you try a fast one, and it don't work, the new owner will bounce your ass out so fast that . . . And you'll never get another manager's job anywhere, not even in the minors."

"I never had a chance at a World Series Championship before in my whole life, Verne, and I might never get another. For five years I had to listen to Prager, do what he said. Now I can do it my way."

Sullivan looked at Bello warily. "I got a feeling I ain't gonna like this."

"Just listen, Verne, don't say nothing till I'm finished," Bello continued, focusing straight on Sullivan's eyes. "We use the relief pitchers. Start Sadoff. Then Ortiz. Finish with Lengo."

"You're crazy. Gone plumb crazy. Relievers? To start?"

"You said it yourself that the game was lost. What would you have done if Muldoon got clobbered in the third inning? You'd've brought in a right-handed reliever, right? How long would he stay in? Two innings? Three innings? Then what? Another reliever? And then maybe our last one? So make believe Muldoon's already been clobbered, only difference is you're bringing Sadoff in with no runs scored and nobody on base. How's that sound to you?"

"Wait a minute, wait a minute. Sadoff, he's a cowboy. He likes to come in to save the girl from the Indians one minute before she's roasted alive. He got to hate the batter—that's why he looks so sore when he throws, like he wants to kill the batter. He wouldn't know what to do if nobody was on base, if the pressure wasn't on."

"So tell him he's saving the Series for us, that he gotta concentrate, make believe the bases are loaded and if he gives up one hit, just one hit, the game's over. Tell him anything you want, feed him raw meat for all I care. And yank him the minute he starts to weaken."

"Maybe—maybe—" Sullivan admitted, "there might, just might, be something in that, but there's also a problem. A reliever can't go more than two, three innings. I only got three relievers. What do I do if—?"

"*Then* you put in Muldoon."

"In relief?"

"Why the hell not? It'll only be for an inning or two. He might even get the credit for the win. Tell him to put everything he's got into every pitch, not to pace himself."

Sullivan looked at Bello, flabbergasted. "And if Muldoon gets hit, put in Padilla?"

"Now you got the idea. We're going to win this one too, Verne. I'm telling you, we're going to win this one."

"I wouldn't swear to that, Butch, but we'll sure as hell surprise the shit out of Dan Zarik."

"That too. Anything that helps us to win."

Sullivan studied his manager for a moment. "Did you ever think of running for president, Butch? I'd like to surprise the Russkies one of these days."

*   *   *

127

"Who's it gonna be?" Dan Zarik asked Rich Martini and Irv Nessen. "Padilla or Muldoon?"

"Butch has got both of them loosening up easy," Martini offered. "I don't think he's made up his mind yet. What do you think, Irv?"

"Muldoon. Gotta be Muldoon. Yesterday he put in Lamburt. Fancy stuff. Today, in case we got used to the slow curves, I'd put in a fastball pitcher to keep us off-balance, if I was him."

"What's the odds against his starting Padilla?"

"Well, it's always possible," Nessen said. "Bello's real tricky. But I'm still betting on Muldoon."

"But it'll be a lefty, right?"

"What else has he got?"

"That's what I wanted to hear. OK, we go with the same lineup as yesterday. Same rules." Zarik looked meaningfully at Rich Martini.

Martini looked uncomfortable. "I'd like to go back to our regular batting order, Dan. We did good all season with it; let's stick with what works."

"No." Zarik's jaw was clenched tightly. "As it is, we're going to have one less right-handed hitter up, and I want to win by a big score today." He turned to Nessen. "You want to pitch Wade, right?"

"He's our best and he's ready. We can't afford to lose two in a row."

"Good. Then when we get to our own park, we can use the DH. So we'll go to Farinella, Devine, and then to Harriman for the final game. You know, he pitched a real good game, gave up only two runs, and if he hadn't been so shocked, so overconfident, if he had thrown to first instead of home when Johnson bunted, we still could've won it."

"Yeah, it was our bad luck that Prager got killed just then," Martini said. "If he was still alive, he never would've let Butch pull those stunts. Maybe it's not right to say it now, but I was counting on Prager to screw things up good, just for insurance. Whoever killed him, he didn't do us any favor."

128

"You don't think it was one of us, I hope," Zarik said. " 'Cause if you do, you better keep your mouth shut. I need all my players."

"Then you're thinking what I'm thinking, Dan." Martini looked embarrassed. "Anybody with sense wouldn't have . . . But Len Carter was in right field just about the time . . . and he's so crazy that—well, you never know."

"Forget it, Rich," Zarik ordered. "No Boomer had anything to do with it, and no Boomer was in a position to do anything. Got it?"

"Sure, Dan, I never would've said . . . This is just between us. But what I mean is—you're not going to play Carter today, are you? Grasso got a good hit yesterday just when we needed it."

"Carter plays," Zarik said grimly. "Same strategy as yesterday. *Exactly* the same. But this one we're going to win, come hell or high water."

"You're not going to pitch again today?" Marc asked incredulously.

Warren Lamburt threw a perfect knuckleball to Jerry Leach, the third-string catcher, who was barely able to follow the erratic pattern of the ball and had to shift his oversize glove to knock it to the turf. "OK, Jerry," Lamburt said, "that's enough for now."

Leach looked relieved as he got up from his crouch; nobody liked catching a knuckleball pitcher. It was too easy for the catcher to miss the ball completely and get an undeserved passed ball charged against him. Or worse, to let in the run that could lose the game. Or to break a finger as he grabbed, barehanded, for the unpredictable ball. A knuckler was slow only compared to the ninety-plus miles-per-hour speeds of modern-day fastball pitchers. At sixty-plus, a knuckler, caught wrong, could still ruin the already gnarled throwing hand of any big-league catcher. Or crush the skull, Marc thought, of a Samuel Moultran Prager. Though it was doubtful that a knuckleball had been used. Even at thirty feet, it would be surer to throw a fastball. Or, more likely, snap a throw without even thinking. No way, at that distance, to miss a white face in a dimly lighted tunnel.

"What made you think I was going to pitch today?" Lamburt asked, walking over to where Marc stood on the edge of the turf. He held the ball with his fingernails, knuckleball grip, and kept throwing it firmly into the pocket of his glove.

"I was surprised to see you warming up."

"I was practicing," Lamburt said. "To keep control of a knuckleball, you have to practice every day. Even then it's hard to get it over the plate. If it doesn't look good, nobody's going to swing at it. Why? You going to do a story on me?"

"Sure. Two stories. The first one is a feature on your terrific success in changing your career at forty, and adding maybe another five years to staying in the majors. Give me a few good quotes; I got the basic story practically written already in my head."

Lamburt thought awhile, then said, "I guess the main thing is to understand, to really realize, that you change. That you're changing all the time and you have to take it into account. What you lose in physical ability you might gain in something else. When I was a kid, all I wanted to do was to power the ball past the hitter so fast he couldn't even get his bat around in time. Then I learned to keep the ball at the batter's weak spots. I studied every batter and learned what he could hit and what he couldn't, and I made a card for him. Then I practiced control. Not just in practice, not just on the field, but all year round, wherever I was, I managed to throw at a target—on a wall or something—every day and to study my cards every night. A few years back, before anyone else knew it, I saw I was losing velocity. I figured out that the best way to lengthen my career was by . . . I love baseball; I never want to do anything else but be around baseball. But if I kept up my old ways instead of changing, accommodating to my new condition, I'd soon be out of baseball. And the kids who saw me—they'd only remember me as a half-assed pitcher who got sent down. So I figured out that if I could throw easy, I'd get to stay in baseball, active, for a lot more years."

130

"So the knuckleball was a deliberate choice? By scientific analysis?"

"Observation. Pitching fast, especially hard-snapping curves, is real hard on the elbow. Look at Carlson. At his age he already has arm trouble, gets massages between innings. The older pitchers, you ever see them smoking a ball past the hitter? No way. Throw slow, last longer. That's me."

"If you'd been practicing, as you said, for some years, why did you hardly ever throw a knuckleball in a game until yesterday?"

"Verne and Butch wouldn't let me. Or Krumanski. They were afraid, I guess, of what Prager would say. Do. And they didn't really believe . . . The first time—I didn't even warn Walt Krumanski, because I knew he'd stop me. It was in practice and I figured . . . Walt grabbed the ball—instinctively, I guess—barehanded, and split his finger. Verne told me if I ever pulled a bush trick like that again, he'd . . . He was right, too; I could have cost us the pennant." Lamburt looked truly penitent.

"Then how did you get permission to throw it for the first time in a World Series game?"

"I didn't. The rule book says that the pitcher who's designated on the official batting order has to pitch till at least one man is out or reaches base. They couldn't take me out until I pitched to the first batter."

"You staked your whole career on getting one batter out?"

"I had decided to do it that way long ago. My career with the Bandits was gone anyway; no way was Prager going to let me stay after my contract was up. The way he kept after me, what he said on TV . . . he was just looking for an excuse to get rid of me. So I took the chance. The Boomers are a power team. Once they take off—if I pitched the way I usually do, they could easily put together homers back-to-back and wipe us out. The only chance we had was if I could catch them off-balance, fool them. They weren't looking for knuckleballs—and even if they were, knuckleballs are damn hard to hit—and it worked."

"So it's lucky for you that Prager got killed?"

Lamburt flushed right up to his thinning blond hairline. "You don't have to put it that way, Marc. We all . . . what I mean, I don't want to see anybody ki— dead, but Mr. Prager . . . if he— that is, what he did was—he really *interfered*. Screwed things up. I think he would have had Butch yank me right away." Lamburt paused, then realizing where the question had led him, added, "You've got to give Corey Steen credit too, for signaling Butch to leave me in."

Marc was not to be put off. "So you benefited from Prager's death?"

"Well, in a sense—that is—sort of. We all benefited, the whole team. But that doesn't mean that one of us . . . Everybody hated him, not just the Bandits."

"I've interviewed people who said you were in a position to throw the ball that killed Prager at the time he was murdered."

"I was all over the field. Nobody knows exactly when Prager was killed. There must've been a hundred guys who could have been . . . Why are you asking me these questions? Who made you a detective?"

"If I break this case, it'll be the biggest story to hit Brooklyn since . . . Look at it this way, Lamburt. You're a pitcher. You're known for your control. You could hit a *dime* at thirty feet. Prager hated you and was going to throw you out in such a way that no one would hire you for anything, just like he did to Len Carter. Only you're old and Carter was a kid; you can't work your way up again. Prager insulted you and treated you like dirt every chance he got. You hated him and he stood in the way of your staying in baseball and going out a hero. You were in the right place at the right time. It's only a matter of days before Lieutenant Danzig arrests you. Why don't you give me the story now, the whole story? I'll write it up nicely, sympathetically, make you look like a hero, and tell the whole truth about what a bastard Prager was. You'll be sure to get away with it."

Lamburt looked angry, really angry, for the first time that Marc could remember. "You better not talk that way about me," Lamburt said, his normally soft voice harsh. "I don't want Lieutenant Danzig, or anybody else, bothering me right now about anything, or thinking I might be the one who killed Prager. You make any more trouble for me and . . ." Lamburt threw the ball, fastball grip, hard into his glove. Very hard. The ball made a loud slapping sound, just as if it were hitting the side of someone's head. Marc's? A distinct possibility, Marc realized. Understood. Comprehended. *Knew*.

18

Dan Zarik clutched the copies of the Boomers' batting order to his chest and tried to catch a glimpse of the Bandits' lineup as Butch Bello handed the papers to the umpire. The umpire calmly kept the sheets against his chest and held out his hand to Zarik. Reluctantly, the Boomers' manager handed over his batting order. The umpire compared the papers, then gave each manager a copy. To one-up Zarik, Bello didn't even bother to look at the Boomers' lineup. Zarik took one look at the copy in his hand, then another, and exploded. "What the hell are you pulling now, Butch? You gone crazy?"

Butch faked surprise. "Something wrong, Dan? You want me to change it? OK, Dan, just tell me what you want."

The umpire just looked at the two managers patiently. "Time to play ball, gentlemen," he said.

Marc was as surprised as Dan Zarik to see Russel Sadoff on the mound, and immediately had the lead for his story: "Butch Bello pulls another fast one."

Sadoff glared at the leadoff batter, Sam Battles, as though he would like nothing better than to put the first ball into Battles's left ear, *through* Battles's left ear and out the right. The wild-eyed pitcher, unshaven, his left cheek bulging with a double chaw of tobacco, hair uncut and uncombed, would have frightened off three muggers at midnight. With a hard ball in his hand and real hate in his heart, he made batters stand several inches farther from the plate than they usually did. Battles took up his normal stance and waited for the first pitch.

The first pitch, at ninety-five miles an hour, came right at the batter's head. Battles dropped to the ground, fast. Dan Zarik came charging out of his dugout, screaming to the umpire. "Get that maniac out of there before he kills somebody!"

The umpire waved Zarik back. "Come on, Dan, that was a wild pitch and you know it. If he wanted to bean Battles, he'd've thrown behind his head. Save the acting for when it's important." Zarik stopped just short of the ump but before he could say another word, the umpire added, "Don't delay the game unnecessarily, Dan." Zarik, fully aware of the penalty for deliberate delay of game, took a deep breath and marched back to his dugout.

Battles got set in the batter's box, unconsciously a bit farther back than before, and went down on two called strikes and a futile swing at a low fastball that caught the outside corner.

Len Carter, up next, crowded the plate, but was careful not to project his head into the strike zone. Sadoff put five fastballs low and inside, so close that when Carter hit the last pitch on three-and-two, it was near the handle, a weak grounder and an easy out.

Jason Cordray hit a long high fly to center field that Pete Rigdale had plenty of time to get under. Side retired.

In the Bandits' half of the first, Kullman went down on called strikes, Smootra stuck his bat in the way of one of Forrest Wade's fastballs and hit a little blooper over third that shortstop Emilio Leon caught, and Bob Coffee hit a hard line drive right into Isaac Brown's hands for the third out.

The Series was shaping up into a pitchers' duel, Marc thought, surprised. With a great slugging team like the Boomers and a strong-hitting team like the Bandits, the first game had ended up 2–1, and the second was beginning to look just as tight. He punched some notes for Monday's column into his portable terminal.

In the second inning, Isaac Brown hit the first pitch for a line-drive double that bounced off the center-field wall. Looking *really* angry now, Sadoff struck out Herb Hedstrom, the Boomers' catcher, on three sharp-breaking curves and got Mel Wheatley to hit one into the dirt, moving Brown to third and bringing up Art Casey, the powerful first baseman. Art waited out the count to two-and-two, then hit a towering fly to right field that Mario Demarco caught with his back to the wall for the third out.

Demarco, first up for the Bandits in the second, got a big hand and a lot of girlish squeals. With one ball, he leaned into the second pitch and hit a long drive into the right-field bleachers that was foul by a foot. He fouled off the next pitch, waited out another ball, then hit a clean single between first and second.

The crowd went crazy as Reuben Johnson, the big first baseman, came to bat. Johnson let a ball and a called strike go by, then swung mightily at the third pitch, fouling it off behind the plate. He let a ball go by, then his bat barely caught a roundhouse curve and popped it to short right field. Len Carter, who was playing deep, could not get to it in time, and Demarco pulled up at third.

Men on first and third, none out, and catcher Corey Steen up. The stands were screaming for a score, for first blood, for Steen to put one away. Forrest Wade bore down hard, and Steen, with orders to hit away and avoid a double play at all costs, swung for the fences at three good pitches and struck out, bringing up Rigdale, a dangerous hitter. After a glance at his dugout, catcher Herb Hedstrom stood up and Wade threw four wide ones to give Rigdale an intentional base on balls, loading the bags to make a play at any base possible, and bringing up shortstop Pancho Rivera, the weakest hitter on the Bandits.

Immediately Bello called for Barton Magee, a long-ball hitter, to pinch-hit. Wade tried for the corners, but as a lefty, his pitches were coming in to a right-handed hitter and he could not make them too good. The first two were called balls, as Magee waited patiently for a good one. The next pitch was right down the middle, knee-high. Magee golfed it, a very high fly to deep center. Cordray caught it on the warning track and immediately threw it to Wheatley, the cut-off man at second, who instantly faked a throw to first. Rigdale, who had taken a long lead, slid back to first as Wheatley threw to home plate, holding the slow Johnson at third. Demarco had easily scored the first run of the game.

Two out, men on first and third again, and Sadoff, the pitcher, up. Pinch hitter Oley Peersen came to the plate, a left-handed batter and the strongest hitter Bello had left. What's he going to do, Marc wondered, if he has to use another pinch hitter later on in the game? Evidently Bello wanted another run badly and was willing to risk everything on a single throw of the dice, though a more conservative manager might have put in shortstop Cubby Banneker, a right-handed hitter and the natural replacement for Pancho Rivera, saving Peersen for another emergency.

Peersen looked carefully at two very low balls and a strike, fouled one off, and did not swing at the next ball. As Wade went into the last pitch on a count of three-and-two, both men on base were off and running. Peersen, knowing the pitch had to be good—no way was Wade going to load the bases by a walk with the top of the batting order coming up—he swung and hit a sharp double over first, just out of reach of Len Carter's desperate dive. Johnson and the speedy Rigdale scored as Peersen rounded second to draw a throw, then pulled back fast.

Dan Zarik walked out to the mount to confer with Wade and Hedstrom. They talked for a full minute, then Zarik walked back to the dugout and Wade prepared to pitch to Joe Kullman. On the third pitch, Kullman hit a hard grounder to Emilio Leon at deep short. Leon whipped it underhand to Art Casey barely in time to get Kullman, and the second inning was over. Three hits, three runs, no errors, and the Bandits were leading the Boomers by a score of 3–0.

The Bandits took the field, with weak-fielding Cubby Banneker replacing Rivera at short and reliever José Ortiz, a right-handed curveballer, pitching. Emilio Leon was first up. Ortiz toyed with the bottom of the Boomers' batting order, using wide-breaking slow curves that barely clipped the corners of home plate, striking out both Leon and Wade easily. When Battles came to bat, Ortiz started snapping his curves. The count went to three-and-two as Battles hit two fouls before striking out on a sinker for the third out.

Smootra led off the second half of the third inning by poking a short fly over first, but Len Carter had been quietly sneaking in as Wade wound up and as soon as the ball left his hand, Carter dashed in, coming close enough to barely get under what looked like a sure hit for Smootra. One down. Coffee hit a high fly to center that Cordray gathered in easily. Demarco went down on three hard swings. No runs, no hits, no errors; end of the third.

Len Carter started off the fourth by slapping a hard grounder along the third base line for a single, then took a long lead off first. Jason Cordray, a dangerous hitter, was at bat and Ortiz kept throwing pickoffs to keep Carter close to the base. On the second pitch to the plate, Cordray leaned on a curve and hit a long fly to left, which was caught by Coffee, but Carter had tagged up and slid into second inches ahead of the throw. Isaac Brown, the Boomers' most powerful hitter, came to bat. The Jersey side of the stands were screaming for a homer and the huge Brown looked as if he were ready to oblige. Ortiz threw sinkers low and close to the right-handed Brown. With the count three-and-one, Brown stepped back on the next pitch and tore a hard double off the left-field wall, scoring Carter and bringing up Hedstrom. One out, one run in, a man on second.

Ortiz, anxious not to give Hedstrom a good one to hit, walked him, putting men on first and second. Wheatley came to bat and hit the first pitch to short. Banneker fumbled the ball before he flipped it to Kullman at second, allowing time for Hedstrom to barge into the second baseman and break up the double play.

With men on first and third and two out, Art Casey, who had hit a home run the day before, came striding confidently to the plate. Ortiz threw four very wide balls, which loaded the bases and brought up the weak-hitting Emilio Leon. Dan Zarik called for Henry Grasso to pinch-hit. Grasso hit the first two balls foul, long drives into the right-field stands. With the count two-and-nothing, Ortiz began putting extra snap on his curves and kept the ball wide of the plate, but Grasso didn't bite. He caught the next pitch on the end of his bat and dribbled a grounder down to third. Smootra picked up the ball, stepped on the base, and the side was retired. Score: 3–1 in favor of Brooklyn. Zarik put in Ray Blaine to play shortstop.

Reuben Johnson swung late to hit Wade's first pitch into short left for a single. Steen drove a hard line drive to center that Cordray hardly had to move to catch, and Johnson barely got back to first in time. Rigdale hit a sharp single to left, and Isaac Brown's perfect throw almost caught the slow Johnson at third. Banneker came to bat with two men on and one out. He hit a hard drive to deep short. Blaine dived at it and, from his knees, flipped the ball to Wheatley at second to force out Rigdale in a great play. Men on first and third with Ortiz up. Bello immediately put in Yancey Wilder to pinch-hit, a lefty but the best he had remaining. Working carefully, Wade got two strikes on Wilder, then picked off Johnson on third. End of the fourth and the score still 3–1.

Left-handed fastball pitcher Marty Lengo was not the best choice to put up against the Boomers, but he was the only reliever Bello had left. Jim Conroy, pinch-hitting for Wade, hit a long double off the left-field wall, to bring up the top of the batting order.

Battles hit the first ball sharply between first and second. Reuben Johnson barely got to it and tossed the ball to Lengo to put Battles out, but Conroy advanced to third. As Len Carter came to bat, the Bandits' first and third basemen pulled in to protect against a bunt. Carter obligingly faked a bunt, then poled a long fly to left, which scored Conroy.

Cordray walked, Lengo trying too hard to keep the ball low and inside. Isaac Brown was given an intentional pass, bringing up Hedstrom with men on first and second and two out. Lengo was putting everything he had on the ball, really smoking them in. Hedstrom took the first strike and missed the second. On the next pitch Hedstrom hit a hard liner to short center field. Pete Rigdale ran in for it, dived, and caught it as he slid on his belly. Side retired and Rigdale got a big hand from the Brooklyn crowd. The score was now 3–2, Bandits.

Lefty Mal Tucker took Wade's place. Bello had used so many

pinch hitters that only Willard Madison, an average hitter, was left to pinch-hit for Lengo. If anyone got hurt, Bello would have to use Jerry Leach as a pinch hitter, leaving the Bandits without a spare catcher, but Bello was determined to win this game, no matter what it took. As long as there was a chance to score another run, Bello would grab it and cross the other bridges when he came to them.

Madison hit Tucker for a bloop single over third, bringing up Joe Kullman, the top of the batting order. Kullman waited out Tucker and got a base on balls, advancing Madison to second. On the third pitch, with both base runners taking off, Smootra dropped a perfect bunt along the first baseline. One out, men on second and third, Coffee up. Coffee hit the first pitch to deep center, scoring Madison easily, with Kullman taking third. Clean-up batter Mario Demarco stepped into the batter's box, with two out and a man on third. The crowd, which usually went wild at the mere sight of the handsome outfielder, was quiet, waiting, begging silently for their hero to hit a home run. Demarco hit the first pitch, a tremendous blast, high to right field, clearly going over the wall. Len Carter sped back, back, and, at the last second, jumped against the wall to catch the ball over the top of the fence. A groan went up from the bleachers. Three out, one run, one man left on base, and the score 4–2 in favor of the Bandits.

"What do you want to do next?" Verne Sullivan asked. "Padilla or Muldoon?"

"They're killing the fastballs," Butch Bello replied, "and they're killing our lefties, but we only got lefties left. So it gotta be Padilla."

"I was going to save him for Hague Stadium. You put Muldoon in against the Boomers in their own park, you're asking to see a record for homers."

"We're still ahead by two runs, and I want this game. Only four innings to go. I got to have a pitcher with good stuff. Padilla will have plenty of rest by Game Five."

*　　*　　*

Wheatley, the first man to face Padilla, went down swinging at a sinker. Art Casey hit the first pitch out of the park, his second homer of the Series. Ray Blaine struck out, and even though there were two gone, Dan Zarik put Norbert Smalls in to pinch-hit for Tucker. Padilla pitched carefully for the corners and, at three-and-two, fooled the anxious Smalls with a change-up. Now it was 4–3, Bandits.

Zarik put in right-hander Hernando García to replace Tucker, though Tucker had not faced the entire Bandit lineup. Big Reuben Johnson went down swinging, Corey Steen hit a hard single over second, Pete Rigdale hit a short single to right, sending Steen to third and bringing Cubby Banneker up. The infield pulled in to cut off a run, but Banneker swung away and hit a hard grounder to Ray Blaine. Blaine flipped the ball to Wheatley, who touched second and jumped up and threw to Casey for the double play before Rigdale could crash into him, ending the sixth inning. Score still 4–3.

In the beginning of the seventh, Battles caught a curve before it broke and hit a long fly to left that Coffee caught easily. Carter walked and stole second, but Cordray hit a line-drive to Banneker for a double play and the third out.

In the bottom of the seventh, Bello, with no pitchers left, had to let Padilla bat. Padilla swung late at three fastballs. Kullman swung late to hit a Texas Leaguer over first for a single and moved to second on a slow ground ball to first by Smootra. Coffee came up with a potential run on second and two out. He hit the first pitch for a clean single, his first hit of the day, scoring Kullman. Demarco walked, bringing up Johnson, who already had two hits for the day. Zarik ordered an intentional pass to load the bases and get to Steen. Steen hit a long fly ball to center that Cordray caught over his shoulder. One run, two hits, the Bandits leading 5–3.

Brown, the first man up, got his third hit, a long single to center. Hedstrom hit a slow roller to first for an easy putout by Johnson, but the throw was too late to catch Brown at second. Wheatley hit a grounder to Smootra, who caught Brown in a rundown. Casey, who was having a great Series, hit a double, scoring Wheatley and bringing up Blaine, with the tying run on base. Padilla went all out and put Blaine down swinging. It was 5–4, still Bandits.

Rigdale, who had gotten on base today each time he came up, drew a walk to keep his record going. Banneker hit a short fly to center and Rigdale had to hold on first. Padilla struck out and Kullman hit a long fly to left that Brown caught near the fence. Still 5–4, Bandits.

For their last chance to win the game, Zarik put in right-handed Luther Young to pinch-hit for García. Young hit a low drive to center that Rigdale caught in a dive. Battles hit a single to right and Len Carter singled to left, with Battles taking third. On the first pitch to Cordray, Carter stole second, without a play. With one out and the go-ahead run in scoring position, Padilla, working the corners carefully, brought the count to three-and-two. Cordray did not swing at the next pitch, a widely breaking curve, and the umpire jerked his right thumb over his shoulder for strike three. Dan Zarik was out of the dugout and at the ump almost as fast as Cordray was, but to no avail.

With two out, Brown, who had gotten three hits this day, was walked intentionally. Bello was gambling the game on getting Hedstrom and Wheatley out before Casey had a chance to bat. Padilla was keeping the ball low and the infield was in at the corners with short and second at double-play depth. Hedstrom took the first two pitches, a ball and a strike. He swung at the next, a low slider, and drove a hard grounder at third. Smootra caught it on his belly and dived to third base. Three out! Game over! Bandits win 5–4, and lead the World Series 2–0.

The Brooklyn crowd went crazy; the Jersey crowd packed their tents and silently stole away, vowing to kill the bastards when they got them on their own turf.

Marc typed in the story on his portable terminal, the straight story as it happened, and the Monday column. He decided to hold the column on Warren Lamburt for Wednesday and wrote—it almost wrote itself—about the daring innovations, and the luck—no way to deny that—of Butch Bello. And how fortunate the Bandits were that

Sam Prager was not around. Not that he could put it that baldly, but it was clear in every paragraph, that the Bandits were doing better without Prager than with him.

No way to question anyone else today, in spite of what Danzig had said about speed. To go into the Boomers' locker room now would be like walking through a graveyard at midnight on *Walpurgisnacht*. To question Dan Zarik, and especially Len Carter, about Prager's murder would be putting his head in the lion's mouth at feeding time. Nor would the Bandits' locker room be any better. Neither Verne Sullivan nor Butch Bello would take kindly to having their celebration interrupted with reminders of murder. Tomorrow was an off day, and Marc would use that time to interrogate Zarik and Carter. And to straighten out Julius Witter about what Marc's duties were. And his hours. And to tell Nelda Shaver her new deadline. And to ask, *beg* her, to smooth Lucy Stone Valentine's feathers. And to sign a nonaggression pact with Dahliah. And to put off Lieutenant Danzig for another couple of days. Somehow. And— did he leave out anything? Oh, yes, and to solve the Prager murder. So what else was new?

19

"You're home early." Dahliah, sitting stiffly on the couch, smiled, too sweetly. "How nice."

"It's the usual time," Marc said warily. "Seven-thirty."

"Actually"—she looked carefully at her watch—"seven-twenty-eight. It was very gracious of you to rush—I know how *terribly* busy you are on *important* matters—just to please me because you know how much I like having a leisurely Sunday together with you. And *two* minutes early. A lovely anniversary present. Thank you, darling."

"I really *did* rush. I got home as soon as I could."

"I know, dear, and I understand. You're trying to give me a taste of how wonderful life will be when we get married. How much time we'll have together. Love *and* companionship. Never being alone. Always being able to *count* on someone. Very thoughtful of you, Marc; I would never have been able to figure it out by myself."

"There *was* a game today," he said, trying to keep the irritation from his voice. Would women *never* understand? "A World Series game. That I had to write up. And some human-interest stories. And my regular Monday column. Most reporters would consider that two day's work, but on *The Sentry* . . . Plus an interview with Warren Lamburt about the murder. Which reminds me, I have to call Lieutenant Danzig."

"You spoke to him last night—isn't that enough? And ruined the evening. A Saturday night, at that. Wouldn't you rather talk about some important things? Have a meeting of the minds, if nothing else?''

"It'll just take a couple of minutes, darling, then we can have the whole evening to ourselves without interruptions. If I don't call him now, he'll call me later. At just the wrong time. Like last night.''

She stared at him suspiciously, then leaned back against the couch. He took that to mean agreement—or, at least, not disagreement—picked up the phone, and dialed. Danzig answered immediately, as though he were waiting anxiously for the call. "I interrogated Warren Lamburt,'' Marc announced.

"OK. What did you find out?'' Danzig snapped.

"First I have to talk to all the others, compare stories, see what discrepancies there are, where—''

"Cut the crap, Burr. You trying to teach me my business? Just tell me what you found out.''

"Well, Lamburt is a definite possibility. He has a strong motive for hating Prager and he was in the area at the time of the murder. He's perfectly capable of hitting Prager at that distance with a real hard fastball and no one would notice if he threw a ball into the tunnel at that time.''

"I got that already, Burr—why do you think he's on the list of suspects? Don't tell me what I already know; tell me what you found out that's new.''

"Lamburt isn't the sweet, friendly guy everyone thinks he is. He has a real bad temper. He could easily have seen Prager in the tunnel and, without thinking, thrown the beanball, just the way I figured it might have been done. In fact, when I showed him he had motive, means, and opportunity, he threatened—sort of threatened—me.''

"He threatened to kill you? Hey, that's great.''

"What's so great about my getting killed?''

"It shows we're getting someplace. Now keep your eyes open, so if anyone throws anything at your head, I want you to see who it is.''

"Are you crazy? What good will it do to see him if I'm dead?''

Danzig sounded annoyed. "The point is, if anybody, not just Lamburt—even if you don't recover—if *anybody* tries to get you, it shows I'm on the right track, and when two crimes are committed in the same case, you got the *modus operandi*. That means the way the murderer operates. Then I got him. All that's left is to put on the pressure till he cracks, then I take him downtown and sweat him a little, then—''

"Yeah, I got the picture. I get killed and you get a promotion. Great. OK, I'll let you know who kills me, even if I have to write his name in blood. Call you tomorrow.''

"Wait, wait. Who else did you talk to?''

"Nobody. It was a busy day.''

"Just one guy you talked to? With four suspects left?''

"Tomorrow's a travel day; no game. I'm set to see a couple of them already.'' Marc hung up.

"What's this about your getting killed?'' Dahliah asked, looking worried. "You didn't tell me you were—''

"It's all right.'' Marc tried to smooth things over. "That was just for Danzig's benefit. Make him think I'm doing my best to help him solve the case.''

"And you aren't?''

"Well, yes, I am, I have to, but I'm not going to risk my life for . . . Besides, I thought you were mad at me.''

"Damn right I'm angry, yes, but I want you alive to suffer if I decide to kill you myself, painfully. Or in case I need you for something, in case I decide that there's still *some* potential in staying with you a little longer.''

"Oh, there is, there is,'' he said fervently. "Lots.''

"What you said, that there's no game tomorrow. Does that mean we can have the day off? I only have morning classes on Monday.''

"Well, not exactly. I have to go to Jersey to do a couple of stories on the Boomers. And to interrogate—interview—Dan Zarik and maybe Len Carter—about the Prager case.''

"Can't you do that in the morning?''

"Yes, sure, but I have a date with Butch Bello at one—George Blondin set it up—and I have to go to the office in the afternoon to see Nelda Shaver about persuading her to—getting her page done by Thursday close, and you know how touchy she is.''

"You're an editor now; just *tell* her. You can do it by phone. From what you've told me about her . . . I don't want you even going *near* that—that succubus."

"Well, it isn't just a matter of . . . there is something I have to do in person. With her."

"The only thing that has to be done in person is . . . and that, I don't want you doing at all. With anyone. Especially *her*." Dahliah glared at Marc. "What is it that you have to do with Nelda Shaver *in person*?"

"It's not *personal;* it's business. One of her interns, Lucy Stone Valentine, is thinking of—"

"*Lucy Stone*? Do you know who Lucy Stone was?"

"Yeah, sure. One of the women's libbers, right?"

"One of—? She just happens to be practically the founder of the whole women's movement. She was one of the first suffragists, organized the first women's-rights convention, refused to pay taxes because she had no representation, kept her maiden name, everything. She's my idol. I'd like to meet Ms. Valentine. I'm sure I'd like her."

"Yes, well, I don't think that's necessary. Nelda can handle . . . that's what I have to see Nelda about."

"You're not going to let Nelda Shaver do anything to that poor innocent young woman, are you? If you do . . . You're the assistant editor, Marc. It's up to you to protect—"

"No, no, it's nothing like that. Actually, under the right conditions . . . Nelda has already promoted her." Dahliah still seemed unsatisfied. "It's—Valentine is going to sue Mr. Witter and *The Sentry* and—in that order. That is, she feels—there's a possibility it may be considered legally—only from a certain viewpoint, that is— sexual harassment."

"I thought so," Dahliah said smugly. "We all go through that, and it's time to teach them a lesson. I've always suspected Julius Witter; he's a dirty old man if I ever saw one. Marc, you have to help this poor girl win her case. If you need any legal advice, I know several good lawyers at the school, women, naturally, who'll be glad to take the case. *Pro bono*, of course. Won't cost Valentine a cent. By the time they're through with Julius Witter, he'll wish he had never *seen* Lucy Stone Valentine, much less harassed her. I'm so proud of you, Marc. For a long time I've wondered if . . . not that you're not nice to me, but in your work—sports is such a *macho* thing—and the influence of all those ignorant men . . . but now I'm sure you really understand—living with me has definitely raised your consciousness—and it makes me feel about you . . . Don't worry about tomorrow, just do what you have to do to help that poor girl win her case, no matter how long it takes. We'll make up for it some other time. Tonight, maybe? Now?'' She kissed him warmly. ''Yes, tonight. Right now, OK?'' She kissed him again.

Marc kissed her back. This was not the time to clarify any misconceptions. What the hell: Eat, drink, and be merry, for tomorrow we die.

20

"Luck," Dan Zarik stormed, "that's what it was. Luck, pure and simple. You wait here," he tossed over his shoulder to Marc and stomped over to the batter's box, where Rich Martini was working with Len Carter. "Not your goddamn head," he yelled, loud enough for Marc to hear. "You want to get killed, wait till the Series is over. Any way you get on base is just fine, but if you're willing to get hit, twist away from the ball toward the catcher so you get it in the back. Can't you learn this dum-dum not to stick his head over the plate, Rich? That's asking for it." He waited until Martini demonstrated the movement, then came back to Marc. "OK. We were talking about how lucky the Bandits were."

"You want me to write," Marc asked, "that the Bandits were just lucky? For real?"

"Hell no. You trying to make me look bad in the papers? All I want to do is teach you something so you don't make it look like Butch Bello is a genius and we're all dopes."

"He did win two games he wasn't supposed to win. And he did do it by pulling some very unusual tricks."

"That's it, exactly. Unusual tricks, shit; they were bonehead plays. The odds were so big against . . . Look, you don't win by always playing it safe, but when the odds are ten to one against . . . Sure the surprise can work in your favor once in a while, but sooner or later the odds catch up with you. Take the play in the first game where Johnson bunted with two out and men on first and third.

There's no way a slow truck like Johnson could beat out a bunt, even if he bunted to third. And that's if he bunted good, which he ain't exactly famous for. What Bello was gambling on was that Harriman would throw a ball that could be bunted, that Johnson would bunt it good, that Smootra would get home fast enough, and that Harriman wouldn't throw the ball to first to get Johnson out."

"Well, yes," Marc admitted, "but he was a little trickier than that. Harriman had to throw it low and inside because Johnson swung for the fence on the first pitch. Then the ball was bunted to Harriman's left, which means he had to transfer the ball to his right hand to throw. Then Harriman was facing third and he saw Smootra take off when it was too late to change his pitch and all he would think of was the run coming in. Also, as a righty, he had to half turn to get to the bunt. Put it all together, and it wasn't as bad a gamble as you make it seem."

"Bullshit. Bello was doing it like a magician. Watch this hand while the other one steals your wallet. Psychology. Maybe the other things aren't all that bad, but his main trick was to totally surprise Harriman, fool him into throwing home instead of to first. What are the odds against that kind of play working? Ten to one? More?"

"At least that, but why not?"

"I'll tell you why not. Johnson—what's the odds on his getting a hit? One out of three? A single would bring in two runs. A homer, three runs, and wrap up the game good. Any manager with sense would've let Johnson swing away."

"Well, maybe, but it worked."

"It sure as hell won't never work again. After I got through reaming Harriman . . . And the second game. Where he started relievers. You know how many pitchers he used in that game? Four, that's how many. And pinch hitters? He used up almost his whole roster, that's how many. He had to put in one more batter, there was practically nobody left. And if he needed one more pitcher, who was he gonna put in? Muldoon? We would've killed him. Carlson? Who he's saving for tomorrow? Verne Sullivan? Ha! He don't have a good reliever left for tomorrow; Carlson better pitch a full nine innings."

"Relievers only pitch a couple of innings. If he has to, he can put in Ortiz or Lengo again."

"Maybe. Then again, maybe not. We'll see. What I'm trying to tell you—Bello's a faker. Does it all with mirrors. And there's a limit. Sure he gets away with it, maybe, for one game or two games—but it don't work forever. Sooner or later, the odds catch up with you."

"Are you saying that you'll win the next four games? That Bello's shot his wad?"

"If you don't quote me, for damn sure. He's come to the end of the road. From now on, he's got to play serious baseball. And if he does that, we gotta win."

"There's another way to look at it, Dan. If you were managing a team that was outclassed, where if you played straight baseball you were sure to lose the Series, wouldn't you try anything you could to win?"

"Hell yes, sure, I probably would've done what Butch did, more or less, but for me it probably wouldn't've worked. All I'm trying to show you is that he was real lucky, that's all. Not just on the field either. If Prager hadn't cashed in his chips, you can be damn sure he'd've been on the phone every five minutes, and we would've won both games. By big scores. I know; I used to work for the bastard."

"You think Butch had something to do with that?"

Zarik sighed. "I wish to God he had; get rid of both of them at the same time. But he didn't. I was watching the right side of the field when Butch came out and he just came out, that's all. Didn't throw nothing."

"I know. I was watching too. Where were you at the time?"

"Near the Bandits' bullpen. I was hoping to get a look at their pitchers, but only Lamburt came out when we was going off the field. I saw Butch coming out as I was going back along the right-field line."

"So you were in a position to have thrown the beanball at Prager yourself?"

"Hey, fifty guys were in a position. I went over all this with the cops."

"Yeah, but those fifty guys didn't have a reason to kill Prager like you did."

"I never wanted to kill him. Ask any of my guys. Yeah, I always was talking about humiliating him, beating his brains in by a big score, but not killing him."

"You still have a good arm, you hated him, and you had plenty of opportunity."

"Everybody on the field got a good arm, everybody had plenty opportunity, and half the guys in the stadium hated him. So why pick me? You looking for a story, it gotta be a Bandit."

"I'm checking the Bandits too; got an interview in Bello's office at one. But couldn't it also be an ex-Bandit? You or Len Carter, maybe?"

"Hey, leave Len alone. He's nervous enough as it is."

"If I don't talk to Len, Lieutenant Danzig will. And I'm a lot easier to talk to."

"Danzig already did, and I don't want him bothering my boys again. OK, you can talk to Len, but for God's sake, don't give him a hard time. He's the only one on this team got the real spirit. I need him real bad."

"Don't worry, I won't do anything to get him mad. I need myself real bad."

"I'm busy," Len Carter said. "I have to take batting practice soon."

"It's only for a few minutes," Marc said. "I'm in a hurry too; want to interview Art Casey and Isaac Brown, then I have an appointment at Butch Bello's office at one. Tell me, Len, why did you hate Sam Prager?"

"I played for the Bandits," Len Carter said. "That's why." Carter was gulping down a black coffee as they sat on the bench in front of his locker. "Anybody who ever played for the Bandits had to hate Sam Prager."

"So it seems," Marc said. "But not as much as you do. Did."

"Depends on how Prager screwed them, and how much. Me, he

really went out of his way to put the boot to." Carter was clearly growing angry just thinking about it.

Marc tried to tread delicately. In the field, next to the big men on his team, Len Carter looked slim and small, but sitting at this locker, next to Marc, he looked huge and tough and dangerous. "What exactly did Prager do to you? All I hear is he sent you down to the minors."

"All? That's all?" Carter glowered and reached for another cup. "Listen, I was the most promising rookie they had. I was tough and fast and good. I thought fast and moved fast. Good reactions and good brains. And aggressive. Another Pete Rose, they used to say. Maybe not as good a hitter, but I got on base plenty. And I stole too. Put me leadoff, and I could score on a bunt and a short single. I'm a smart fielder too. You saw how I robbed Smootra of a sure hit in the second game? Well, that's how I was with the Bandits."

"Yeah, I saw you play, but what I heard was, you didn't listen to the coaches. Or the manager."

"That's part of the bullshit Prager's pimps put out. George Blondin and the rest of those PR jerks. I got respect for Bello and Diggins; they know the game. What I can't take is a bastard like Prager losing us games with his stupid telephone. I hate losing games, specially games we could've won." He finished his second cup of black coffee. "So I told him off. What an asshole he was. Plain. In front of everybody, at one of his jerky meetings in the locker room. That was the end."

"He sent you to the minors. So? Lots of rookies get sent down. You came back, didn't you?"

"Yeah, sure, four years later. He didn't just send me to one of the Bandits' farm teams. Like for seasoning, which I didn't need. No. First he got the grapevine going, telling everybody, all the other owners, I'm a troublemaker. That's one thing owners don't like: a troublemaker. Then he gets them all to agree to waive me. So I end up in the American League, with a Class A team, where I don't know nobody and nobody knows me. With a label as a trouble-maker, which means any time I say something, do something that

153

would be perfectly OK for somebody else to do, I get it in the neck. And fined. And my wife is pregnant. You know what it is to be a baseball wife in the minors? Hell, that's what it is. Absolute hell. We almost got divorced, that's how bad. And the money? Hell, you could get more pumping gas. Four years it took me, and here I am, alternating right field with Henry Grasso on the best team in the majors. Why? Because I'm faster than I used to be? My eye is better? My batting average is higher? Hell no. It's not as good. I lost four years, big-money years, on account of that lying bastard. I could've been a star, a real big-money star. Now I got to bust my ass just to play when lefties are pitching. That's what Prager did to me.''

"So you hated him enough to kill him?''

"Hey, what're you getting at?'' Carter's narrow little eyes were bloodshot. "You trying to make trouble for me too?''

"No, no, just want to get information.'' Marc inched a little farther away. "I just want to know if you saw anyone, from where you were in right field, at the end of practice, throwing a ball into the tunnel on that side.''

Carter looked at Marc, disgusted. "You're stupid, you know that? You're stupider than that cop, Dancer. How the hell's somebody gonna throw a ball in the tunnel with a million guys watching, huh? How the hell's he gonna know when Prager is right in the right place, huh? How the hell's he gonna see in the dark to hit Prager, huh? You're stupid, that's what.''

"Isn't it possible that he just happened—the guy who threw the beanball at Prager—just happened to look into the tunnel at the right time? Accidentally? And saw Prager coming out of the waiting room? And the light from the waiting room, the open door, lit Prager enough for the killer—the guy—to see him? And that he snapped off a throw—it was only thirty feet—without thinking, that caught Prager in the head? And nobody noticed? Isn't it possible? I mean, if the guy really hated Prager, and he had fast reactions—like all ballplayers—without thinking . . . ?''

Marc edged away as Carter stood up, boiling, and grabbed a soda bottle by the neck, like a club. "You trying to say I did it? Me?

154

When I got my chance again? You trying to send me back to the minors?'' Carter grabbed for Marc, but Marc scooted away just in time.

He half ran to the entrance of the locker room and paused there. "Thanks for the interview, Len. I'll see you tomorrow at the game.'' Marc turned and went out. It was time to get away; the interviews with Casey and Brown could wait. In fact, with Carter all red-assed, it was time to get out of Jersey. Though he would have to be there tomorrow, for the third game. Maybe when the Boomers won, they'd all be in a better mood. He'd be a little early for his interview with Butch Bello, but with Len Carter in his present mood, and lots more bottles available . . . He didn't want to keep looking over his shoulder to see if Carter was the one to brain him from behind. And he wondered how Carter knew how hard it was to see Prager in that tunnel.

21

"You know where Butch is?" Marc asked Earl Diggins, who was supervising batting practice.

"You're early," Diggins said, not taking his eyes off Walt Krumanski, who was scheduled to play in Game Three on Tuesday. Marc noted that Krumanski was still favoring the right middle finger that Lamburt's knuckleball had split. "Butch said you was supposed to meet him in his office around one o'clock."

"I got away early. Is he around?"

"Someplace. Last I heard, he was going to see Popeye Pitney. Why don't you go to his office and wait? He'll be there sooner or later."

"If I don't find Butch," Marc said, "that's what I'll do. If you see him, tell him I'm here." Marc went into the tunnel near the home-team dugout.

Skinny old Popeye Pitney was sitting at his desk, going over a list. "Hey, Marc." The trainer's smile was really friendly. "Just the guy I wanted to see."

"I'm looking for Butch. Diggins said he might be with you."

"Was, not twenty minutes ago. Don't know where he went. Verne Sullivan might know. Or Lamburt. Butch was having a heart-to-heart talk with both of them when he came in here. Wanted me to check some vitamin pills for pepping up the players before a game. Like I heard your friend Pusher Rybek gives out."

"What's the matter, you run out of greenies, Popeye?"

"That's not funny, kid." The trainer's wrinkled old face twisted in a frown. "I hate amphetamines. There's nothing'll ruin a player quicker except maybe dope and steroids. I catch anybody with amphetamines, I'll kick his ass around the bases in front of the whole team, I don't care how big he is."

"Just kidding, Popeye, don't take it so seriously. Unfortunately, I don't know what's in Pusher's secret formula. All I can tell you is that it really works—gives you a lift that lasts two quarters of a football game."

"Yeah, that's just what I need. I've been experimenting with B-fifteen on myself and it works some, but it's not enough."

"What I do when Pusher's not around," Marc said, "I make up my own formula. A hundred milligrams of niacin, one fifty of B-fifteen regular, one fifty of B-fifteen time release, two thousand of C with bioflavonoids, six desiccated liver pills, and two tablespoons of honey. I take it with eight ounces of cold water fifteen minutes before a gymnastics workout. It's not as good as Pusher's formula, but I feel light and strong for a good hour after. Of course, I take a full regimen of vitamin and mineral supplements every day, and I'm sure that has something to do with it."

"Yeah, and you're also a vegetarian—maybe that comes into the picture too. Fat chance I got to make those animals into vegetarians. Half of them eat chicken-fried steak and home fries for breakfast. Or chili con carne."

"Well, you could suggest it to them. Can't hurt. I wasn't a vegetarian till I met Dahliah. I don't know if it's the diet or having Dahliah, but in the past year I've been healthier and happier than I've ever been in my life."

"Probably both. Why don't you do the right thing and marry her? This younger generation—I don't know what's got into you. At your age, I already had teenage kids."

"It's not me, Popeye. Her career—she's a college professor . . . I'm sure it'll work out. Meanwhile I better go look for Butch. Let me know how you like my formula."

"Diggins said you was to meet Butch in his office. Why don't you wait there? It's coming on to one and if you both go wandering around looking, you'll just keep missing each other."

"Yeah, I might as well do that. Does everybody in the Dome know my business?"

"You tell George Blondin to set up an appointment for you, everybody in the whole U.S. of A. is gonna know your business."

Marc wandered slowly along the main corridor toward Bello's office, passing the various colored doors and musing on the morning's interviews with Dan Zarik and Len Carter. Both of them really hated Sam Prager and both of them were in a position to have thrown the ball at the time Prager was killed. Both of them had strong arms and could have thrown the ball hard enough to crush Prager's temple, and no professional baseball player could miss Prager's head at thirty feet. Carter, if he got angry enough, could kill, and Zarik—well, it was not necessarily an attempt at murder. It could just as easily have been an expression of anger, to show Prager that he couldn't hurt people and get away with it all the time, that Prager too was vulnerable, and could be hurt.

Without conscious thought, Marc turned left into the dimly lighted tunnel and stood in front of the recess at Bello's office, undecided whether to go in now or to continue to the field for a quick look around for Butch. He heard a *something* and from the corner of his eye saw the ball streaking at him, and the top of his head exploded in a brilliant, blinding white flash.

22

Marc opened his left eye a little and it was Popeye Pitney bending over him, gently feeling the spot on top of his head. The swelling. It *hurt*. "Hey," Marc protested.

"Shut up and lay quiet," the trainer ordered. He felt around some more, still gently, then harder. Marc winced. "You'll live," Popeye said, "but there might be a fracture. Probably a bad concussion. You lay quiet and I'll get you to the hospital."

"The ball," Marc said. "It came from my right. I saw it. From the inside, not from the field." He turned over. Popeye tried, gently, to hold him back, but Marc got on his hands and knees and attempted to stand up.

Popeye pushed him against the wall. "Just sit for a while. You might have a concussion. How do you feel?"

"Weak. Dizzy, a little." The ball was to his right, against the wall, about ten feet away, toward the field. Just like with Prager. "I'll be all right."

"Follow my finger." Popeye held the point of his finger in front of Marc's nose and moved it slowly from side to side and up and down as he stared into Marc's eyes. "Keep looking. You feel anything like things are sliding down? Like a waterfall?" Marc shook his head and winced. "OK. Now look at the main corridor. Keep looking, get your eyes used to the dark. Now, fast, look at the entrance to the field." Marc squinted at the sudden brightness. "Well," Popeye admitted, looking into Marc's pupils, "maybe nothing real serious, but I ain't a doctor. You don't want to stay here, I'll get you to my place and you can lay down while I call an ambulance.''

Marc struggled to his feet, with Popeye helping him. "Yeah, I'll lie down for a while, but no ambulance. I have too much to—"

"You know, kid, I got enough tape in my place to make you look like a mummy. Either you go to the hospital standing up—they take you pretty fast in the emergency room; I'll go with you to make sure—or you go on a stretcher, taped up like a strait jacket, but either way you go."

They started walking slowly toward the main corridor, Marc's arm over Popeye's shoulder for support. Suddenly Marc stopped. "The door," he said. "It's open." Straight ahead of them, the black door to the equipment-storage room was wide open, the weak light from the corridor barely graying the near portion of the pitch-dark room. "I remember now. It didn't register before, but I remember now. The door was open. That's where he was hiding, waiting for me. The murderer."

"Yeah." Popeye walked with Marc into the equipment room. "Maybe you're right." He switched on the light. Marc flinched again, covered his eyes, and gradually took his hand away. "And there it is," Popeye said.

Directly in line with the door, about six feet into the room, was a pitching machine, its long cable plugged into a wall outlet. The little red "Ready" light was on. The machine looked somewhat different from those Marc had seen in the past—newer, smoother, more streamlined. "He was here waiting for me," Marc said. "When he saw me . . . All we have to do is find out who was in here at that time and—"

"Nope," Popeye said, unplugging the power cord, "if he was in here, he would've unplugged the machine and rolled it back to where it belongs. Maybe even sprinkled dust on it. For sure, he would've closed the door and we would've never known how he did it. Also, if he was in here, he might have to stay ten, fifteen minutes; how would he know exactly when you got here? From the field, or in the corridor, he could take a quick look into the tunnel every once in a while and if he saw you, that was it. The guy who set this up, he could have been anywhere the machine could hear him. Inside or outside, long as it's no more'n a hundred feet.''

"But how . . . ?''

"Prager bought this one about four years ago. Super special. Trouble with the old machines is, they kept pitching. Long as there was balls in the hopper, ready or not, they'd keep pitching. And they weren't too accurate either. This one—if you was the batter or the batting coach—you had a little control box on your belt with a supersonic signal, like for your VCR—there's a computer in that machine—and you could make the machine pitch one ball every time you pushed the button, or to keep pitching every few seconds at whatever timing you called for. You could set it for high, belt-level, or low, inside or outside, or random, so's you'd never know what's coming next. Or when. Pretty accurate too. You could aim it when you set it up, and it'd come real close to where you wanted it. Damn good for a machine, but they're out of business now.''

"If it's so good, why aren't they using it?''

"Ask Earl Diggins that. The main thing is, this is the killer. This and the guy who aimed it and who pushed the button when you got into position to be killed. That beanball was four inches lower, you'd be next to Prager in the morgue right now. These machines could throw a lot harder than any pitcher ever lived, including Bob Feller and Sandy Koufax and Nolan Ryan all put together. And it was aimed to kill. Trouble is, there's no way to make the machine more accurate than maybe six inches any direction. Depends on where the seams on the ball is when it's pitched and the exact weight of the ball and how much it's scuffed and who knows what-all else ''

"Yeah,'' Marc said sarcastically. "I guess this is my lucky day.''

Popeye walked around the machine. "Yep. See how clean it is? Drops of oil on the floor? This machine was cleaned and *tested*. Take a look over there. Another pitching machine's in the back, the regular kind, over to your left. Covered with dust. This one's it; no doubt about it." He walked over to the door and pulled it closed. "Just what I thought. The hinges been oiled." He swung the door open again. "Quiet as a grave. And drops of oil on the floor. And here"—he pointed to the strike—"the hole's been stuffed with paper. He could've gone in and out without the key."

The trainer started to remove the paper stuffing, but Marc stopped him. "No. We've got to leave that for the police."

"But he can do it again. To anybody. Butch or anybody who walks in his office. Or out."

"In. It has to be in. Prager was hit on the right side, which means he was going in at the time. Just like me. Don't worry. The police— after they examine everything, they'll take it away."

"Hey, I hope . . . You tell 'em it got my fingerprints on it because . . . I don't want nobody to think I had something to do with—"

"There won't be any fingerprints on the machine or the balls. This guy was careful. Real careful." Marc thought for a few seconds. "What we have to do is determine where everyone was at the time. Whoever was in position to signal the machine—no, not just that. He had to see me. That's the important thing, cuts it down a lot. He had to see me to know when to make the machine throw. If he could see me, whether from inside the building or outside, he was automatically in position to make the machine throw the ball. So the question is, Who was where when?"

"Hell, Marc, there must have been a hundred guys who were near right field alone, plus one or two guys who might have been walking through the corridor. How you gonna know?"

"If he wasn't in this room, there's only three, four places he could have been. Outside, in the right-field area or near the bullpen. Or in the main corridor, toward the offices or toward the equipment rooms."

Popeye looked doubtful. "That don't sound like much help."

"We can narrow it down still more. First of all, the equipment room. That's usually kept locked, isn't it? Who has the key?"

"The security guys, the cleaning crew, Eddie the Miser, who's in charge of equipment, the top executives, the maintenance crew, the grounds keepers' crew—a million guys. Even I got a key."

"Where do you keep it?"

"You don't think I . . . ? Hell, Marc, I might've hated Prager, but I like you. Besides, if I was gonna kill somebody, I'da done it to his face, so he could see who it was, not with a machine."

"If I thought it was you, Popeye, would I be talking . . . ? Where's the key?"

"Where I always keep it. Top left drawer of my desk."

"So anybody could have borrowed it for a few minutes?"

"I guess."

"That's no help then. Let's start eliminating. How long was that fancy new computer-pitching machine used?"

"Less'n one day. Diggins didn't even want to try it, but he had to, 'cause Prager spent a hell of a lot of dough on it. After one batting-practice session Diggins said if he ever saw it again, he'd take a bat to it."

"So it had to be somebody who was on the Bandits then and is still on the Bandits now."

"Nope. Had to be somebody who was around then and is around now. Don't have to be a Bandit."

"But that's impossible. No one who isn't a Bandit is on the field now."

"There's fifty guys who ain't on the team who're on the field right now."

"You mean reporters and photographers?"

"And grounds keepers, security men, guys bringing in the sandwiches and beer and stuff, executives, publicity guys, you name it."

"But none of them would want to kill me. None of those guys would want to kill Prager either." Marc thought of George Blondin. "Well, maybe one or two."

"Maybe. Maybe not. But whoever killed Prager might want to

kill you too. You been snooping around a lot. It ain't that hard to get into the Dome if you know where everything is. And if you hide in the far end of the main corridor back by the storage rooms, off in one of those little passages, hell, you could stay there a week and nobody could find you.''

"What are you getting at, Popeye?"

"Just that it didn't have to be a Bandit. I remember the day clear, the day this here pitching machine was delivered. That was the day Dan Zarik was brought in and Prager told Bello to go home.'' Marc was speechless. "And the day Len Carter was sent down. The Prager massacre. Four years ago, it was, a couple of months less. And either one of them, they might have thought it was fitting to kill Prager with his own fancy new machine.''

Marc took this in, digested it, then said, "No. I don't believe it. It had to be a Bandit. Who else would know where I'd be, when?''

"Just about everybody who could hear straight when Diggins called me.''

"That must have been just before I got to the Dome. What time did I leave your office when I went here?''

"Didn't look. Twenty to one. Ten to. About.''

"You're telling me it could have been anybody? That's a hell of a lot of help.''

"I'm telling you it didn't have to be a Bandit, that's all.''

"We should have searched everybody. Had them searched. See who had a controller in his pocket.''

"Not with this guy.'' Popeye went over to the racks on the wall, found a small metal box, and opened it. "Yep, should be an even dozen. One of the controllers is missing. That proves he wasn't in here when . . . If he was, he'd've put it back in the box. By now, that gadget—it's no bigger than a pack of cigarettes—it's buried in a pile of garbage, or even gone out of the Dome. With the fingerprints wiped off. That's if it's still in one piece. Shouldn't be hard to hit it with a bat and flush the pieces down the toilet.''

"The police might find the pieces.''

"Might. And if they do, what'll that tell them we don't already know?"

"What I should do is check who was in a position—"

"Forget it, Marc. First of all, if it was Zarik or Carter, and they was hiding in the far end of the corridor, you'll never know it. They'd be long gone by now. Far as the Bandits are concerned, if you think it was one of them, hell, everybody was in the right position around that time, more or less. You think, on the field, anybody's gonna remember who was exactly where, or even if he was around, at an exact time? People are always going to the toilet, going for drinks, getting something outta the locker. Always."

Marc ran his hand over his head. The lump was *big*. And painful. "What time did you find me? Why were you there in the first place?"

"Verne called me on the bullpen phone, asked if I seen you. Said Butch would be delayed and to tell you not to worry, he'd be there about half past or a quarter to. Soon's I got the call I went to the office, figuring you'd be in the waiting room. Found you about five, ten after, more or less."

"So I was out for ten to twenty minutes?"

"Just about. That was some hit you took."

"Yeah, I still feel it. Tell me, who do you think did it?"

"My guess—and it's a guess, you understand—is Dan Zarik. Len Carter don't have the smarts for anything this complicated. He'd just as soon take a bat to your head from in front. Sooner."

"Thanks a lot, Popeye. Anybody but a Bandit, right?"

"You asked me, I told you." His voice softened. "You ready to go to the hospital now? You might have a concussion, even if major signs ain't there. I'll go to the hospital with you, if you want, though you look fit to go by yourself, now."

"OK, I'll go, right after I'm finished here. Do me a favor." Marc handed Popeye his little auto-focus camera and stood next to the pitching machine. "Just look through the viewfinder and press the button. The flash will go off automatically. Take three shots, about two seconds apart." Popeye did as he was told. "Now take some shots of me on the floor, exactly the way you found me.'' He led the way to the entrance to Bello's office and lay down.

"What's that for?" Popeye asked.

"I'm still a reporter," Marc said. "Julius Witter'll kill me if I don't bring back some pictures."

Popeye positioned Marc, moving his arms and legs slightly. Exactly how Prager was lying, Marc thought. After the last flash, Marc got up easily, feeling much stronger. "I'd like to go to your office; I want to call Lieutenant Danzig." Better here than from home, where Dahliah would worry. The lump on the top of his head was still throbbing painfully.

"OK. Lean on my shoulder."

"I'll go by myself, thanks. You stay here."

"Why? You want to be private?"

"Yeah, but I also want you to stay here to make sure nobody moves anything until Danzig gets here. Besides, I know you're dying to tell Butch and the others what happened so they can get their stories straight. I can't interview them now; Danzig will have my head if I talk to them before he does."

"It wasn't a Bandit," Popeye muttered. "It was a Boomer."

Marc took advantage of the opportunity to write up what had happened—an exclusive story of how an intrepid *Sentry* reporter was almost killed in a dastardly murder attempt and the discovery of how it was done, hinting that Prager had been killed the same way. Marc didn't give much credit to Popeye Pitney, partly because he didn't want the killer going after him too. In spite of what Popeye had told him, Marc still felt it was more likely a Bandit who had set the deadly trap than a Boomer. He plugged the telephone wire into the back of his terminal and sent the story in to *The Sentry* computer, attention Witter. Marc was definitely not in the mood to talk to the editor directly. He'd go to the office after he got out of the hospital, assuming the doctors didn't insist on keeping him there for observation. As soon as the modem was done sending, Marc rang Danzig and told him the whole story, starting with his interrogations of Dan Zarik and Len Carter, and ending with the attempt on his life.

"Hey, that's great," Danzig said.

"What the hell's so great about it? I almost got killed. Four inches lower and—"

"Yeah, yeah, OK, but it shows the pressure is getting to him."

"Not just to him. To me too."

"That's the way it's supposed to work. If you was acting, it'd show. Spoil everything. Now we know we've got to get him before he gets you."

"Thanks for explaining it to me."

"Hey, you put yourself in the picture yourself, didn't you? With your fancy reporter's tricks? You got what you deserve. But you got my sympathy, kid. All of it. For real."

"Thanks. That helps a lot." Marc's head was hurting even more and Danzig was not helping very much.

"Zarik didn't threaten you, did he?" Danzig asked. "Even a little bit?"

"He's a manager," Marc said. "Too smart for anything like that."

"But Carter did?"

"He was ready to take me apart right then and there. I practically had to run for my life. He's a real nasty character."

"How long after that were you hit?"

"About an hour and a half, maybe more. I stopped to eat."

"So either one of them could have gone to Brooklyn and set up the machine?"

"Easily. If he knew how to get into the Dome."

"He knew. They both worked there, didn't they?"

"Would one of them go all the way to Brooklyn just to kill me? Wouldn't it be easier to wait till tomorrow, when I'm in Hague Stadium?"

"Maybe he was in a hurry to get you before you told me who he was."

"But I don't know who the killer is."

"It's still early; talk to Bello and Sullivan today, right after I get through with them. I'll soften them up for you."

"Can't. I have to go to the hospital. Get X-rayed. Popeye Pitney thinks I might have a fractured skull."

"You don't. I can tell; you're still talking fresh."

"You're all heart, Danzig."

23

"No bandages?" Julius Witter asked. "No stitches? Not even your head shaved?"

"Sorry to disappoint you," Marc said, "but it's only a mild concussion."

"A good newspaperman would have insisted on bandages. Lots of bandages. That would have made a good picture for the front page. Captioned SENTRY REPORTER ATTACKED BY MAD KILLER."

"I did send you an exclusive on the attack, an eyewitness report. With heartrending quotes from the victim."

"You missed seeing the killer. If you had kept your eyes open, as a good reporter should, you might have seen someone lurking about with the pitching machine's controller in his hand and solved the case right then and there. What were you doing, Burr, daydreaming? Or plotting new ways to extort more money from me?"

"I was planning the interview with Butch Bello. I have to tread very carefully with him. One wrong word, and he can stop the players from talking to me at all. Then what use would I be to the paper?"

"I would have found it difficult to notice the difference." Witter sighed. "Very well, I should have known I couldn't depend on you. Give me the film." He held his hand out. "It's getting late."

"What film?" Marc asked innocently.

"You persist, Burr, in the face of continued failure, in thinking you're able to outsmart me." Witter snorted. "Ha! That will be the day." He put his hand out again. "The film please. The pictures you so carefully posed and had Jake Pitney take, with the intention of misleading our highly vulnerable readers." Marc took the cartridge out of his pocket and put it on the editor's desk. "I am amazed," Witter continued, "that you forgot we have several other reporters, good ones, in the Dome, who were prevented by your confederate Pitney from getting near where your body had lain, your unfortunately *uninjured* body. And who, therefore, pressed Pitney to explain why."

"I didn't forget; I just thought that these pictures would be worth a raise."

Julius smiled cruelly. "Why don't you think about finally getting around to doing what I'm paying you to do as assistant editor? In fact, you had better do it this afternoon before it slips your mind— your little talk with Nelda Shaver."

"Nelda? Now? I'm not in any shape for Nelda."

"This happens to be one of the rare times Nelda graces our humble office with her presence. However, if you're really not up to it, I'm sure she'll be happy to entertain you tomorrow night in her luxurious reconstruction of Madame Pompadour's boudoir. Worth seeing, I assure you. Perfectly authentic in every detail."

"You've been there?" Marc said in astonishment. "With *her*?"

"Many times," Witter assured him. "On business, of course. With my reputation for probity and rectitude, no one would even think . . . You, on the other hand, if Dahliah were ever to find out that you went there, even if you started out with only the best of intentions, given Nelda's well-deserved reputation . . ."

"I'll see Nelda now," Marc said. "No need to go into detail." He stood up wearily. His head was throbbing worse than before. "I'll lay down the law to her."

"Nelda is a profit center," Witter said, "as I've explained to you many times, and Mr. Heisenberg likes profits. Please keep that in mind when you talk to her. Be gentle with her, and polite, and do not annoy her in any way, or even irritate her slightly. And after you've settled the Lucy Stone Valentine matter—which is your primary task; please don't forget that she intends to sue *me* too—if Nelda's not too fatigued, you may bring up your *suggestion* that she get her copy in on Thursday close rather than on Saturday, as she is accustomed to doing. And fix your tie. Nelda likes men who are neat.''

Inappropriately for a working newsroom, but perfectly befitting her image as Nelda Shaver, she wore a black cocktail dress cut low behind, even lower before, and just a tiny bit too short. There were none of those telltale little lumps in the smoothness of the clinging cloth at her bosom that indicated a bra, nor were there any lacy black hints at the cleavage to indicate what supported that great cantilever of siliconed flesh. And her legs . . . they were lovely, Marc had to admit, as which woman's would not be in long—very long, he noticed, as she uncrossed her legs and crossed them in the other direction—very sheer black silk stockings—with seams running exactly vertical from the backs of four-inch-heeled patent leather *thé dansant* pumps.

Her lips were a perfect dark-red Cupid's bow, glossy and smooth and hard as lacquer, slightly parted, the sharp tips of the pure white, too-even teeth barely visible. Skin smooth and well filled, looking hard and rigid as marble, caressed, not by her usual auburn pageboy fall, but by a heavy hang of long, gleaming, black hair that swung back and forth with her slightest motion. Her eyelashes, thick and heavy with mascara, masked her languid eyes—green this day— with mystery, her carefully drawn high-arched brows flaring to an Oriental uptilt at the ends.

Nelda put her bony, porcelain-white, blood-tipped hand out to him. ''Why Marc,'' she said, ''so nice of you to come to see me.'' Her voice was soft, low and sexy. ''It's been *ages*.''

Her hand was still out. Marc took it gently and bent—it seemed called for—to kiss it. She turned the hand slightly and ran its palm up his left cheek. ''That's sweet, Marc. I love men who know the way a woman needs to be treated.'' Her hand slid down, around, then up the right side of his face, caressingly. He took the hand—

it was *hot*—and held it in both his hands; better there than on his face in a glass-enclosed office. Where everyone—he didn't dare check—was . . . Marc sat down so that the wooden lower panels of the enclosure would hide most of what—*whatever*—Nelda would do that shouldn't be done.

"Not there, darling," Nelda said as he took a chair. "Where I can see you." And "where I can see you" Marc understood, and moved to a chair directly in front of her. "I'm very busy today," she said. "I'm extremely happy to see you, of course; I lead such a lonely life. Work, work, work, that's all I do these days, and right now is . . . Can't it wait until later? This evening? When we can take our time and not be so terribly rushed?" She smiled slightly, very carefully, as though afraid to crack her face.

"I'd love to, Mrs. Shaver"—at her moue, he immediately corrected it—"Nelda, I mean, but this is business."

"I *always* do business at home. Most of what I do at home is business." She sighed pitifully. "I'm on the telephone without end. Absolutely without end. That's how I get all the latest news. Anything important, I get a call. So if it's *really* business," she said, smiling archly, "not just one of your boyish tricks to get me *alone* and defenseless . . ."

"It'll just take a minute, then I'll be . . . I have an appointment tonight, so . . ."

"Of course, darling; I understand. I'll make room for you tomorrow night."

"All I want—you know, from now on, I'll be editing 'The Sporting Woman.' Your page."

"Yes, Julie told me."

Julie? *JULIE?* Julius Witter?

Nelda went on obliviously. "Yes," she repeated, "I was overjoyed when he told me. He's all right, I suppose, but he's such a fusspot. An old poop. I told him I needed someone younger, more my age, who would *comprehend* how things are today. The modern woman. What she'd really like. The *sporting* woman. *Her needs.*"

More her age? Witter was a lot closer to . . . "Yes, exactly,"

Marc agreed. "You and I, we feel . . . You're absolutely right. The only thing is—we'll close the page on Thursday evening, OK? That way, I'll have all of Friday to edit it and we'll be secure for the Monday sports edition. Without rushing."

"That's impossible, darling." Nelda showed her teeth. They were firm and sharp and gritted tightly together. Not a bit sexy. "I'd actually like it kept open till Sunday night. You see, I get calls all the time. All the latest dirt and everything. If we close Thursday, there'll be three days' news that just will not be in. Not at all. Only old stuff. *Days* old. Passé. Imagine what would happen to my readership, my reputation. No, no, it's out of the question."

"But Nelda, it's—"

"No, *no, NO!* It's impossible. Completely, totally, *absolutely* impossible. Can't you see that? If I'm not utterly up to date, what is left for me? And what will Mr. Heisenberg think when I tell him? He'll turn *blue*, actually, if I even *hint*. I'm going to make believe you never ever said such a thing. You do understand, darling, don't you? I'm sacrificing my integrity just keeping this from Mr. Heisenberg. He'd be very angry if he ever found out I was keeping *anything* from him. Extremely."

"Yes, but—"

"Don't thank me, darling. I love doing things for people, making them happy. Especially for you. You have such a wistful smile when you're happy. If you want to do any editing, or whatever it is that assistant editors do, and you don't want to wait till Sunday morning, I'll let you come over on Saturday night, after my regular date leaves, and we'll work on your problems together. All your problems. You'll love it, darling, just exquisitely love it. We'll let our hair down and everything."

"Yes, well . . ." Marc knew when he was beaten. "I think we'd better stick with the regular way for a while." No way would he be able to explain to Dahliah that working Sundays was all for her, so that he could be faithful to her. "You can always say no," he could already hear her saying. You can't. Not always. Not directly, that is. Was this how secretaries felt when . . . ? "There's one more thing, Nelda."

"I'm really very busy, Marc," she said coldly. "Can't this wait till Sunday?"

"It's Lucy Stone Valentine."

"That little bitch?" Nelda spat out. "Get her away from me, Marc. Now. Why the hell did that jerk Witter saddle me with her?"

Marc was astounded. Dumbfounded. "You don't—don't—you don't like her?" he stammered out.

"Like her? I hate her. She never does what she's told, she screws up every assignment, criticizes the very *basis* of my page out loud, in front of my whole staff, and refuses to have anything to do with fashion or inside stuff or anything *important*. Says it's *against* women, when everything I do is *for* women. *Everything*. And she thinks she's better than me? Knows better what women like? If she opens her mouth to me once more, I'll—"

"Then why did you hire her?"

"Hire her? Me? A snotty little bitch like that? Who dresses like a— a—punk? In those tasteless, crude, absolutely garish colors? No bra, even?" Well, Marc thought, that solves one puzzle. "That sonofabitch Witter hired her. To fill a quota or something. I specifically asked for a young man. You'd be surprised how much more my contacts open up to a man than to me. And what does that jerk Witter give me? Lucy Bigmouth! Who insists that I call her Ms. Valentine. Thank God she's only an intern, be gone in a few weeks. When she goes, Marc, I want you—you're the editor now, after all—I want you *personally*—you know all the athletes—to help me get a replacement."

"Uh, the fact is, Nelda, that Mr. Witter, my boss, and yours . . . I'm afraid Ms. Valentine won't be leaving in a few weeks. She— that is, Mr. Witter—he told me he promoted her to reporter."

She glared at him, her face finally cracked. "You tell Witter," she screeched, "that he better . . . No, I want you to do it yourself. I'm holding you personally responsible, Burr, *personally*. I want that—that weasel, that horrible *witch* out of here. Fast. One week and that's it. Or else I go to Mr. Heisenberg's *house*. Personally. And when I get through with him, you'll wish . . .'' She stopped suddenly, smoothed her face again. Her voice was quiet, controlled, with a touch of its old sexiness. "I'm sure you understand, darling, how *impossible* it is for anyone creative to work under such difficult conditions. You will take care of it, won't you, darling? There, that's a good boy. Thank you for offering, Marc; you're really very sweet."

24

"Farinella ready?" Dan Zarik asked.

"Couldn't be better," Irv Nessen assured him. "He's had lots of rest and and his fastball is really popping today."

"Trouble is," Rich Martini pointed out, "he's a fastball pitcher. Even though we're outslugging them, twenty-two total bases to thirteen, they got thirteen hits to our twelve. We start giving them a left-handed fastball to swing at, they could easy make doubles out of those singles. I'd think about using Devine for this game, Dan; we can't afford to lose three in a row."

"That's exactly why we gotta use our second-best pitcher," Nessen insisted. "Dennis Farinella got a two-point-nine-eight ERA for the season and Devine's is three-point-six-seven."

"Statistics ain't the only thing, Irv," Martini said. "Harriman gave up only three hits and one earned run that first game and his ERA is worse than Farinella's. We can't use him 'cause he's only had three days' rest after a full nine innings, but look at the facts. We need a right-handed curveballer to win, and next to Harriman, Devine's the only one we got left."

"Wade's a lefty fastballer, and he didn't do too bad."

"He didn't do too good either," Martini replied. "Three earned runs in four innings. Think it over, Dan."

"I'll make my decision just before the game, Rich. Make sure both Devine and Farinella are ready, Irv. Meanwhile, keep in mind that we're not hitting as good as we should."

"They got a better pitching staff than us," Martini said. "Let's face it. What we gotta do is start getting more hits. We got the power, we just ain't meeting the ball."

"It's those crazy tricks of Bello's," Nessen said. "That business with Lamburt throwing knuckleballs and then his putting in right-handed relievers as starters . . . What the hell is he going to pull today?"

"His luck can't hold forever," Zarik said grimly. "Sooner or later it got to catch up with him. He tries to put in Sadoff or Ortiz today, we'll kill them. He's got to go with Carlson. No choice."

"That don't make me too happy," Martini said. "I don't care if he's lefty and fastball, he's the best. We're gonna have a lot of trouble hitting him."

"Yeah, but when we do, those balls will go," Dan said. "It's going to be a batters' duel today, that's for sure. We're the home team for the next three games, and we got another advantage: We'll be using the DH. That'll give us the best slugging average you could put on any field right down the batting order. Half the Bandits can't hardly hit the ball out of the infield, and their pinch hitters ain't much better. So let's go with Farinella, and make sure that we outslug them. Until I say different, I want every man going for the fences."

"Who you going to make DH, Carter or Grasso?"

"Grasso. Carter's been doing great this Series. Keep our lineup as is; it's perfect against lefties, except start Ray Blaine at short instead of Leon; power instead of fielding. And push Art Casey up to fifth place, right after Brown. One more thing: You see Marc Burr around, keep him away from the players. He gave me a hard time yesterday with that Prager business and after he talked to Carter, upset him good. I didn't see Carter for the whole afternoon."

"Yeah, well, you know how Len is when he gets mad. Six beers and three hours is what it takes to cool him off. No harm done. I didn't see you for a couple of hours either."

"That's different. I was doing some thinking. Private."

"Start Carlson?" Verne Sullivan asked.

"Got any other ideas?" Butch Bello responded.

"Well, seeing the fancy stunts you pulled the first two games, I thought you might want to start Ortiz today."

"I wouldn't mind doing it—be worth it just to see the look on Dan Zarik's face—but I can't take the chance. Ortiz pitched two days ago; he usually needs three days' rest. Same for Sadoff, though I'd like to avoid using a fastball pitcher against the Boomers at all."

"Carlson's a power pitcher. And a lefty. They'll be waiting for him."

"Come on, Verne; Carlson's *Carlson*, and he's good and rested too. Sadoff don't compare."

"OK, I'll get the ice packs ready. Just keep in mind, you'll probably end up using Ortiz anyway."

"Yeah, thanks for reminding me." Butch turned to Earl Diggins. "Krumanski ready?"

"Just about. Real anxious. Put away some hard ones in batting practice today."

"How about throwing? They gonna steal on him?"

"Wouldn't say no, but no worse than usual. Depends more on Carlson's windup than Walt's finger."

"OK, start him, but keep Corey Steen warmed up. Also, I'd like to push Pete Rigdale up to sixth place—he did real good last game—and bat Walt seventh."

"Makes sense. Gonna keep Rivera in short?"

"Better put in Cubby Banneker; we're gonna need all the power we got. Today ain't gonna be no pitchers' duel."

"That's for sure. Who's designated hitter, Peersen or Magee?"

"Depends. Who's Zarik going to pitch, Farinella or Devine?"

"If it was me," Sullivan said, "I'd pitch Devine, but I ain't no genius manager, so figure it'll be Farinella."

"Then it'll be Magee. Everything else the same."

"Marc Burr was around before. Said he missed his appointment with you yesterday."

178

"Yeah," Bello sighed heavily, "too bad what happened to him. He's a good kid, but he should've kept his nose outta things like this; leave it to the cops." He looked around the circle of his coaches. "Any of you see anything going on around the tunnel at about that time?"

They shifted uneasily. "All of us was around there," Earl Diggins said. "Passing through, like, back and forth. Hard to say exactly. I didn't see anything suspicious if that's what you're asking."

"That's what I meant. If you think—any of you—if you remember something, don't tell Burr—no sense putting him in more trouble with the killer. Tell the cops, Lieutenant Danzig, direct. And Verne, if you see Burr, tell him he can have that talk with me in the visiting-team dugout, at lunch. Private. No way anybody can get to him there."

Diggins looked shocked. "You think one of us did it?"

"Stands to reason," Bello said. "Who else hated Prager that much? Who else had the chance to set up the pitching machine?"

"Didn't have to be one of us," Verne Sullivan said. "Couple of the Boomers, they really had it in for the boss. With damn good reason."

"Yeah, well I meant one of the ballplayers in the Series. Or coaches."

"Or managers," Diggins said.

"Yeah, that's what I meant," Bello agreed wearily.

"Have a heart, Marc," Earl Diggins begged. "It's almost lunchtime. Besides, I don't know a thing about the killing."

"I'll just take a minute," Marc assured him. "All I want to know is why you turned down that new pitching machine. It seems to me it was a lot better than the old ones."

"Sure, but it still . . . See, the trouble with any pitching machine is that it ain't a person."

"Very funny."

"No, I mean it. See, the guys who make them, they think that it's

179

the ball you're batting against. Which is OK for fun, in carnivals, for amateurs. But in pro ball, it's not the ball you're hitting, it's the pitcher.''

"I read where Ted Williams said he watched the ball until he hit it.''

"That was Williams, and if he says he did . . . An average fastball gets to the place in less than half a second. Takes you almost that long to swing a bat. Scientific tests show the batter has to decide his swing within the first eight to fifteen feet of the ball's travel. In one sixteenth of a second. Nobody can figure out anything that quick. Good hitters, they don't figure, they *know*. They watch the pitcher, the motion, how he holds the ball, how he snaps his wrist, they think about what the count is, what he did in a similar situation, who's on base. Any small clue, you name it.''

"Won't using a machine speed up the reactions?''

"Might, but what's important is to watch the ball release and how it travels the first few feet. A pitcher tries to throw each pitch exactly the same way, but little things show if you know what to look for. A machine pitches exactly the same every time. Same motion, same release. It ruins hitters who maybe could've learned to hit good. That's why I hire live pitchers for batting practice. And that's why Verne uses his best pitchers, sometimes, for batting practice. So they learn to hide what they're gonna pitch, to fool the batters. Pitchers try to fool the batters, batters try to outguess the pitchers. That's what I teach 'em: not muscle, *brains*. Outthink the other guy, that's the game.''

"Are you telling me a pitching machine is useless?''

"Got one use." Diggins grinned evilly. "To kill people.''

Butch Bello was sitting in a corner of the dugout, spooning cherry yogurt from the container. "Figured we'd have privacy here," he told Marc, "and nobody'd be able to bean you. Whatever it is you know, you got somebody scared.''

"If that's what it is, I wish somebody would tell me what I know that's so terrible that he has to kill me to keep me quiet. I sure as hell don't know what it is."

"You think you don't know, but maybe you're just looking at it wrong. Happens to me lots of times. I break my head over—I don't even know what, just that something doesn't figure. Then, just before I go to sleep, it all comes together, and I wonder why the hell I didn't see it before."

"That happens to everyone, Butch, and it better happen to me soon. Which reminds me. You know where Verne Sullivan is after lunch?"

"You gotta leave him alone right now. He'll be working with the catchers and the pitchers till right before the game. After the game . . . if we win, that is. Verne'll bite your head off if we lose—he really hates to lose—so don't talk to him till tomorrow. But if we win, come down and join the celebration. When Verne's in a good mood he'll talk for hours. Just don't spoil the party."

"I want to talk to him about serious things, and I'll never be able to do that while the party is on."

"Come down anyway; you're a Brooklyn fan at heart, ain't you? I can tell."

"I'm not supposed to be, but . . . There'll be some of the other *Sentry* guys there to report the color and I don't want to get champagne poured all over my clothes."

"They don't lay on champagne unless we win the Series; today it'll be just beer."

"Same thing. Look, I'll play it by ear. If Sullivan is in the mood to talk to me, and I'm free . . . Meanwhile, how about talking to me now?" Bello nodded. "Before we start," Marc said, "I want to tell you that I'm really happy for you, Butch. After all these years you have a good shot at the World Championship. Couldn't happen to a nicer guy."

"Yeah, thanks. But I was lucky too." He hesitated. "Is this for publication?"

"Anything you want off the record, just tell me."

"OK. Well, you got to realize: The Boomers, they're a better team. That's off the record. So I had to take lots of chances I normally wouldn't do. Use tricky plays that—well, the odds didn't figure. So today I'm a hero in Brooklyn. If these things didn't work, I'd be a bum and the boss—the management, I mean—they'd be getting calls and screaming to get rid of me even in the middle of the Series. Your paper too, Marc—yes, yours—they'd be writing stories what a dope I become in my old age and maybe Alzheimer's is setting in. It could still happen. We got a two-game lead. I blow it, and I'd get lynched anyplace I showed my face in Brooklyn. And I'd be out of baseball forever. So, sure, I had a run of good luck. But I figured the odds, made the decisions, and it worked. So far. So if we win, I'll take the credit and I'll hold out for a damn good five-year no-cut contract, like some of my superstars got. 'Cause if we lose, I'll sure as hell get the blame.''

"Wasn't Prager—the killing, I mean—wasn't that part of your run of good luck?''

"Hell yes, that's what started it. I know I shouldn't talk that way, but with Prager in the picture . . . you know what he was like. He would have screwed up everything. And if I objected, didn't do exactly what he said, he'd—well, I wouldn't put it past him to fire me and put himself in as manager right in the middle of the first game.''

"Did you see anyone about the time Prager was killed, anyone hanging around the tunnel? Inside or out?''

Bello's face grew red, and for a moment Marc got ready to run, but the manager quietly closed the cap on his yogurt, reached into the plastic bag to his right, and took out another container, vanilla this time. Moving slowly and deliberately, he removed the cap and ate a spoonful before he answered. "You know, kid, five years ago, I would have rapped you in the teeth for asking a dumb question like that. But, little by little, I been learning. Verne Sullivan showed me how. He told me, 'Don't get mad, get even.' I keep on thinking like that, maybe my ulcer might even go away and I could eat regular food again.'' He took another spoonful of yogurt. "So I'll answer your question. I wasn't particularly watching—I mean, who'd figure . . . ? I saw everybody and his brother around there, but I didn't see anybody doing anything suspicious. And I'll tell you something else, Marc. If I did see somebody, I wouldn't tell anyway. Prager—killing somebody ain't right, but with Prager, he had it coming in spades. For years. From everybody who ever had anything to do with him.''

"Including you?''

Bello carefully took another spoonful of yogurt and swallowed before he answered. "Including me,'' he said softly.

25

The press box of the new Hague Stadium, the most beautiful ballpark in the majors, was designed to let reporters work in peace and comfort, separated from the TV crews by truly sound-proof partitions. The ceiling was covered with acoustic tiles and the floor with utilitarian, but tasteful, carpeting. The walls had a six-foot-high wainscot of cork to reduce distracting sound still further and the lighting was bright and unobtrusive. There were electrical outlets every six feet and a telephone connection at every station. This consideration for their needs gave the reporters the feeling that, for once, the management really cared about them. In return, there was engendered in the hearts of all but the most cynical sports journalists a friendly attitude toward the Boomers that often tempered their wholly warranted criticism of the team's owners.

Marc, relaxed and happy, looked down through the in-slanted windows at the perfectly groomed infield, the soft green meadow sliced by the brown base paths, the playing area outlined by the precise white foul lines. The scoreboard reflecting the warming autumn sun, the lightly fluttering flags measuring the gentleness of the breeze, and the buzz of the crowd filtering into the press box brought back to Marc the wonderful days when he first fell in love with baseball, evoking an absurd desire to eat a forbidden hot dog with everything. It was so lovely, so rejuvenating, so overwhelming, so liberating, that he felt innocent again, cared for, protected. To hell with his problems; they could not trouble him on this day.

To hell with Mr. Heisenberg, to hell with Julius Witter and Lucy Stone Valentine and Nelda Shaver and Lieutenant Harvey Danzig, to hell with who-killed-Samuel-Moultran-Prager. To hell with the U.N. and the terrorists and the dictators and the wars and the politicians and everything else the rest of the world thought was important. To an American boy of any age, nothing else counted except what was on the field below. The third game of the World Series was about to start. *The World Series!*

The umpire handed Dan Zarik the Bandits' lineup card. Dan took one look and smiled broadly. "Looks like we're gonna play baseball today instead of fooling around. About time."

"That fooling around put you two games down, Dan," Butch Bello replied and smiled right back. "What excuse you gonna give when we whip your ass again?"

Both Farinella and Carlson were in top form for the first three innings, each facing only nine men, with no hits, no runs, no errors, and no one reaching first. In the beginning of the fourth, with one out, Smootra worked Farinella for a walk and stole second, but both Coffee and Demarco went down swinging.

Battles started off the bottom of the fourth with a single and was sent to second by Carter on a grounder to first. Cordray hit a single over second, putting men on first and third. Carlson worked Brown too carefully and ended up walking him, loading the bases. Casey hit a long single, scoring Battles and Cordray, with Brown going to third, but Carlson bore down and struck out Hedstrom and Wheatley to end the inning with three hits, two runs, and two men left on base The Boomers were leading for the first time in the Series and the Jersey side of the stadium went wild, cheering and screaming for a full two minutes.

At the start of the fifth, Johnson bounced a double off the right-field wall and Rigdale singled him home for the Bandits' first score. Krumanski advanced Rigdale with a slow grounder to third, bringing up Banneker. He hit the second pitch for a clean single, scoring Rigdale and bringing up Magee, the designated hitter. Magee walked, sending Banneker to second. Kullman put his bat in the way of a Farinella fireball and the ball went into short left field, scoring Banneker and moving Magee to third. Farinella bore down, striking out Smootra and getting Coffee on a high foul to third. Three runs on four hits, two men left on base, and the Bandits were ahead, 3–2.

In the Boomers' half of the fifth, Carlson made Blaine ground out. Grasso got a single, but Carlson struck out Battles immediately after. Carter got a single, sending Grasso to third, but Cordray flied out to left and the inning was over. Two hits, no runs, and two men left on base.

In the Bandits' dugout, Verne Sullivan watched Popeye Pitney working on John Carlson's left arm, massaging it with long slow strokes. Sullivan spoke quietly to Walt Krumanski, the catcher. "How much longer?"

"Two more innings, the most. He's losing velocity and they're beginning to get good wood on the ball."

"Ortiz? With two days' rest?"

"He only pitched two innings Sunday. If I can play with my finger, he can pitch a couple more innings. Who else we got that throws fancy stuff righty?"

Sullivan went to the phone and called the bullpen.

In the sixth, Demarco hit a long fly to center that Cordray got under, and Johnson struck out. Rigdale got a single but died on base as Krumanski popped out to third.

Brown started off with a double and went home on Casey's single. Hedstrom's infield grounder forced Casey out at second but Banneker's error on Wheatley's grounder put men on first and second. Carlson struck out Blaine but Grasso poled a homer to right, scoring two men ahead of him.

Bello pulled Carlson and brought in José Ortiz. Ortiz struck out Battles on a sharp curve to end the inning, but the Boomers had scored four runs on three hits and an error and led 6–3. The Jersey fans were hoarse by now, but the level of noise was double that of before.

Banneker got to first on a walk and was sacrificed to second by Magee. Kullman hit an opposite-field double to right, scoring Banneker and bringing up Smootra. On a count of two-and-nothing, Smootra lined a single past third, sending Kullman home and bringing up Coffee.

Zarik put right-hander Hernando García in to relieve. He got Coffee on a sharp curve and Demarco hit a long fly to left, ending the rally with two runs scored on two hits and one man left on base.

Carter got a bloop single off Ortiz and promptly stole second on the first pitch. Cordray was set down swinging hard and Brown came to bat. Ortiz toyed with the outer corners and Brown, trying hard for a homer, struck out on a wide curve. Casey ended the inning with a long fly to center but, at the end of the seventh, the Boomers were still leading 6–5.

In the eighth, García set down Johnson, Rigdale, and Krumanski in order, all on easy high flies to the outfield.

In the bottom of the eighth, Hedstrom led off with a single and Wheatley walked, putting two men on base with none out.

"It's time," Butch Bello said.

"Marty Lengo?" Verne Sullivan asked.

"Hell no—they'll kill lefty fastballs."

"Russ Sadoff did a pretty good job last time out."

"No fireballs. Gotta be all curves and sinkers. They're beginning to get the range."

"That's all the relievers we got left, Butch. Make up your mind fast. I still say Lengo."

"Put in Steve Androvec." Ortiz had a count of two-and-one on Blaine.

"Are you kidding? He's a starter. I thought you were saving him for tomorrow."

"I'll worry about tomorrow, tomorrow. I want to win *this* game."

"This one's lost, Butch; I can smell it. Don't waste Androvec."

"We win this one, we only got to win one out of the next four to be World Champs. I want Androvec."

"He's cold. He'll throw out his arm."

"He got eight pitches to warm up. He does good, he'll have six months to recover."

Working too carefully, Ortiz walked Blaine, loading the bases with none out. The mass of Jersey fans went wild. Bello went out to the mound and pulled Ortiz. Steve Androvec, the skinny curveball artist who was the Bandits' second-best pitcher, came in to face Henry Grasso. Grasso worked the count to three-and-two and began fouling off pitches, putting four in a row into the stands before he struck out on a sinker just at the knees.

Battles was the next to face Androvec. Androvec kept the ball low and Battles hit a slow grounder near second. Cubby Banneker dived for it and tossed the ball to Joe Kullman, who stepped on the bag and snapped the ball to Johnson for the double play, but Battles had beaten the throw. With one run in and two out, Wheatley was on third, Battles on first, and Carter at bat. By now, Androvec's curves were breaking right, and Carter was put out on a weak grounder, pitcher to first. One hit, two walks, one run scored, and the Boomers leading 7–5 after eight.

The Bandits had only one more chance to get some runs. Bello called for Oley Peersen to pinch-hit for Banneker. Peersen waited for the ball he wanted and, at the count of two-and-two, hit a short single into right field. Magee was up next and walked. García was beginning to look worried. Kullman came to bat, and hit the first pitch to the far right corner for a double, sending Peersen and Magee home and tying the score.

"My arm is beginning to hurt," Steve Androvec complained. "I didn't have a long enough warm-up. I need some aspirin. Better make it Darvon; it really hurts."

"I don't want to hear any bullshit," Verne Sullivan told him. "If you're worried about holding the Boomers for one more inning, you

188

can stop right now. All you got to worry about is how to spend all that extra money we're going to win. And how big a contract you get next year if you do good today.''

"Hey, that's not right," Androvec protested. "Mr. Prager promised me, no matter what, I get the same as Carlson got.''

"*Mr.* Prager ain't here no more." Sullivan grinned evilly. "I am. So another thing you got to worry about is what I'm going to do to you personally if I think you're dogging it out there. You lose fair and square, OK. You thrown the game away 'cause you're shitting in your pants, I will break a fungo bat over your yaller head. Got that?''

Smootra came to bat just in time for Zarik to take out García and put in Mal Tucker, another left-handed curveball pitcher. After the allowable eight pitches, Smootra strode to the plate. Tucker was keeping the ball low and inside, and the count went to three-and-two before Smootra drove a high fly to left. Brown camped under it and his throw held Kullman at second.

With one out and the winning run on second, Coffee came to bat and hit a single to left to score Kullman with the run that put the Bandits ahead. Demarco came to the plate, the treble screams of his teenage groupies harmonizing with the lower-pitched howls of the older Brooklyn fans. On the third pitch, he golfed one of Tucker's low pitches into right field for a single and Coffee went to third. As the Brooklyn fans went crazy, Reuben Johnson came to bat. Johnson went down swinging at a wide one and Rigdale hit an easy grounder to third to retire the side, but none of the Brooklyn fans cared. All they knew was that the Bandits had scored three runs and were leading by one and were only three outs away from winning the third game of the Series.

Bello put in Pancho Rivera at short in place of Cubby Banneker. The slugging portion of the Boomers' batting order was up, Cordray, Brown, and Casey, arguably the most dangerous batting combination since Ruth, Gehrig, and Dickey. No way was Androvec going to give them anything good to hit, and neither he nor Krumanski gave a damn that the three sluggers knew he was going to throw only curves and sinkers at knee height. And not over the center of the plate either; a walk did a lot less damage than a homer. With his change-ups and the choice of inside or outside pitches, Androvec had enough variety available to keep the batters off balance.

He wasted a brushback pitch on Cordray, not only to set him a little farther from the plate, but to make him mad and anxious to swing. After that, there were three low curves in a row to bring the count to two-and-two, then he got him on a sinker. Cordray threw away his bat in disgust.

Brown came to the plate swinging his bat confidently, only to go down on four pitches, the last one a called strike. He glared at the umpire, but the ump coolly turned away. Casey at the bat, just like in the old song, and Casey swung mightily at the first three pitches, fouling off two and driving the third to deep center, where Pete Rigdale jumped high to make the third out. The Bandits had won! THE BANDITS HAD WON THE THIRD GAME!

26

Marc finished sending in his story, unhooked his modem, and started to close his portable terminal. Most of the reporters in the press box had already gone to join the victory celebration in the Bandits' locker room. Then he decided to open the terminal again. There was no point in going down to the locker room now. Happy teams were all alike and all victory celebrations the same. He'd end up with beer in his hair, a twelve-dollar cleaning bill, and a story that differed from the others only in style. There was no chance he could talk to Verne Sullivan right now. Maybe in half an hour, but . . . Might as well compose his Wednesday column and be done with it. Again, he would not write about the Bandits' magnificent win; that's what everyone else would be doing. No, a better angle might be . . . Why not focus on the murder? Exclusively. He had to do *something*, and fast. Right now, he didn't have the slightest idea of who the murderer was, or could be, and Danzig was getting impatient. If his column stirred up any reaction, *anything*, that would be better than what he had now. Well, not really *anything*; not another beanball. His head was soft enough where the first one had hit; another beanball might kill him. He bent over the keyboard.

"Aren't you going to get the reactions?" Don Vetnor, a *Post* reporter, and the last one left in the press box, called from the door.

"Not right now, thanks," Marc answered. "I want to wait till it's over, so I can interview— But you can do me a favor, so I don't have to go down into that madhouse myself. When you see Verne Sullivan, ask him to meet me here before he leaves the stadium. I'll wait until he comes and we'll have a quiet place to talk.''

"I'm not going there; I'm going directly to the Boomers' locker room. I find I get much more interesting stories from the losers. If I were allowed to print what Dan Zarik has to say, verbatim . . . And Len Carter? Have you ever heard *him* let off steam? A liberal education in contemporary American usage all by itself. Sorry.'' He turned and left.

Marc picked up the phone and dialed the locker room. After ten rings, still no answer. He then tried the visiting-team PR office. George Blondin answered, breathless. "You're lucky you got me, Marc; I just came back to get more releases. Who would have expected it? Isn't it wonderful? You're going to write a good story on us, aren't you? A *great* story? A long one? We're *news*, Marc—a real upset.''

"Sure, why should I do anything different? Do me a favor, George. Tell Verne Sullivan I'm up in the press box and I want to talk to him. I'll wait. When he's finished gulping beer and telling lies about the good old days, ask him to come up here.''

"Sure, glad to, if I can get to him. He's surrounded by reporters. Everybody is. You should really be down here too, Marc; some really terrific human-interest stories.''

"I work better in peace and quiet, but you can stop sweating, George. The Bandits are going to get four full pages tomorrow; we have five other reporters here today.'' He hung up and went back to his column.

The lead was easy enough:

Sam Prager would have given almost anything to have been at Hague Stadium today. The only problem is, if he had been here today, he wouldn't have wanted to be here, because he would not have seen the Bandits win their third straight Series game. There is no doubt that Prager would never have taken the risks, against all odds, that

Butch Bello did. There is no doubt, in my mind at least, that Prager would have made Bello play by the book and that if he had, the Boomers would now be celebrating their third win in a row.

Marc stopped. How deeply should he go into the murder, tell what little he knew, analyze the evidence, such as it was? Although some bookie might have benefited by knowing that Prager would not be around, benefited by not laying off bets on the Boomers, the nature of the murder itself made it highly unlikely that it was committed by a professional hit man. No, it had to be a personal motive that made Prager's murder necessary. And not just *any* personal motive. If Prager had screwed someone in business, or socially, or was blackmailing somebody, the murderer would not have selected this highly specialized, this technically difficult means of committing murder. In fact, it was highly unlikely that anyone Prager knew outside of baseball would have even known about the pitching machine or how to operate it. Or even how to aim it.

No, it had to be someone who was present four years ago, at the demonstration of the pitching machine. It was clear that Marc's original assumption was correct. When Danzig insisted that Marc knew who the killer was, and Marc, not really thinking, named Bello, Sullivan, Blondin, Lamburt, Zarik, and Carter, he had picked the most likely group. It was almost certain that one of them was the killer. Each had a motive, each had the opportunity, and each knew about the pitching machine and how to control it from a distance. But even in a column, there were limits. He couldn't go ahead and accuse one of them as the killer, not on what he knew now. Nor could he even name them as suspects. Not only would Julius Witter flay him alive verbally, but Danzig would haul him in immediately, for interfering with . . .

How to write the column so as to—without overstepping the bounds of libel—provoke the murderer into making the move that would reveal his identity to Marc? Very funny. Not to *Marc*—to Danzig. Marc would be lying on the floor, dead, his head bashed in, while Danzig would be reading the killer the Miranda—no, that wasn't quite accurate either—while Danzig would be *sweating* the killer. Sweating first, Miranda after—that was Danzig's method. Pleasure before business. Yes, it was all clear. Marc would have to write the column in such a way that the killer would be provoked to attack Danzig. Perfect. Brilliant! Solves all the problems—the immediate *murder* problems, that is; a few others still remained—and once the murder was out of the way, he could put his mind to the important problems: Witter, Nelda, and Lucy Stone Valentine. And Dahliah. Well, all in due time. In fact, if he wrote it right, hinted that only Danzig knew the identity of the murderer and was about to make an arrest . . . With Danzig out of the way, Marc didn't have to worry about who the killer was or what would happen to him if he didn't find the murderer by midnight.

Yes, that was it. Make Danzig the sacrificial goat. Marc was, after all, a professional writer; there'd be no trouble wording the column, ever so delicately, even with a seven-hundred-word constraint, so as to point directly at Danzig. There might be some difficulty, of course, if Danzig survived the Wednesday column and came looking for Marc, but Marc had faith in the murderer. Look how quickly he reacted in killing Prager. Less than two days after the Bandits won the pennant. And how fast he went after Marc. One day after everyone knew Marc was on the case. Practice makes perfect; skill comes with experience. If the pattern continued, Danzig would be dead by tomorrow night.

Marc put his fingers on the keyboard again. Now to lead delicately into the way the brilliant Lieutenant Danzig—who had the best arrest record in Brooklyn, always got his man—had been heard boasting to an unnamed but authoritative source that he had the evidence to put the murderer behind bars within twenty-four hours. Subtlety, that was the key. Machiavellian su— The top of his head exploded in a brilliant, blinding white flash.

27

When Marc painfully opened one eye, Verne Sullivan was crouching over him. "You want me to take some pictures of you?" Sullivan asked, feeling Marc's head carefully. "Popeye told me you like pictures of yourself lying on the floor with your head bashed in."

"Ow, that hurts," Marc complained. "Take it *easy*. Ooh, yeah, that's where he hit me. Right there. In the back."

"Not too bad," Sullivan judged. "Skin ain't even broken. And he didn't hit you; it did." He nodded toward a baseball lying on the carpet several feet behind Marc. "Feel like getting up now, or should I call a medic?"

Marc rolled over and slowly tried to get up. I'm getting experienced at this, he thought. The murderer is losing his grip—that's twice in a row he didn't kill me—and I'm getting used to being beaned. He stood up shakily, Sullivan supporting him lightly. Great. Just great. A few more times and I'll be an expert. "No, no pictures," he told the coach. "Thank you. For your kind offer. You didn't happen to see anyone running down the hall, did you?"

"Nope, and if you ask me did I do it, you're going to be down on the floor again. With a broken jaw."

"OK, you didn't do it. But somebody knew I was up here alone, working. You tell anybody where you were going?"

"George Blondin got a real loud voice. If he was to raise it in a crowded locker room and yell to me that I gotta get my ass up here to interview with you when I got through celebrating, might be a couple hundred other guys also heard him.''

"Yeah, well, that narrows it down a little." Marc sat down, back in the chair he had fallen out of when he was beaned. "It couldn't be a reporter, so it has to be a Bandit." A thought struck him. "Oh, God, no, it doesn't." He shook his head and, immediately, winced. Now there were two places that hurt, one on top and one in the back. "I asked . . . there was this reporter from the *Post*. He was going to interview Dan Zarik and Len Carter. He knew I was alone. He might have told them."

"If he's anything like you," Sullivan noted, "he told 'em. None of you guys know how to keep your mouth shut; that's the trouble with reporters." Seeing that Marc was not going to pass out on him, he pulled over a chair and sat down.

"But how would Zarik or Carter get over here without being seen?" Marc was still trying to cut down the number of suspects. "The stadium is full of people."

"You forget this is their home field? They gotta know the inside of this place like you know your own house. There ain't no way you can be sure it was a Bandit done it." He paused, then asked, "You think a Bandit did it? That what you wanted to talk to me about?"

"Well, it's likely. You hated Prager, didn't you?"

"One of thousands. You gonna to talk to everybody hated Prager, you got a lifetime job."

"Not everyone who hated Prager was at the ballpark in a position to throw that ball at the time the murder was committed. And not every one of those knew all about that pitching machine."

"Who's on your list? Me? Butch?"

"A few others too. Why'd you name yourself and Bello?"

"Because that's what I'm interested in, me and Butch. Anything wrong with that? Me because I'm me, and Butch because he's my friend and the best manager in baseball. At my age, I wouldn't've stayed in baseball if it wasn't to help him. He deserves the best and now, finally, he's gonna get what he deserves."

"Which he wouldn't have gotten if Prager was alive."

"That's for damn sure."

196

"Would you have killed Prager to help Bello?"

"Might. But I never shot a man in the back. And if I would, I'm not all that stupid to do it in the ballpark, where damn fools like you and Danzig would think Butch might've done it. Not if I was trying to help Butch. I wouldn't. Chew on that for a while."

"Did you see anyone who might have . . . ?"

"Prager's dead and nobody's mourning him. Why'nt you just leave things alone, Burr? Third time, he might not miss." Sullivan stood up and just walked away.

Marc sat and thought. If it had been Sullivan who had thrown the ball, which was very likely, he could just as easily have thrown a second ball and completed the job. If he had a second ball with him. Even so, he could have picked up the ball and beaned Marc again; no law said Marc had to be killed with one pitch. Of course, someone could have come along—not very likely at this time, up here, but possible—and seen Sullivan. But how long does it take to throw a ball? Sullivan could always claim he just got there. Then again . . . No, there was no point in going through these exercises. Anybody could have thrown the ball and disappeared in seconds. Or appeared. Like Sullivan. That was the trouble with these simple crimes. Without enough complications, it was impossible to isolate the one person who could have done it. Maybe Danzig was right. Think simple, decide who did it, and then sweat the bastard.

Marc turned to the phone and rang Danzig. "He tried to kill me again. Another beanball."

"Well." Danzig sounded elated. "Who was it?"

"How should I know? My back was turned."

"You stupid bastard!" Danzig sounded really angry. "Didn't I tell you to keep your eyes open? How many times do I have to tell you?"

Marc was angry too. "I'm just trying not to get killed. I know it doesn't fit your schemes, but getting killed is not tops on my agenda today."

"I'm getting very tired of you, Burr. You're just too goddamn stupid to follow orders and I can't break this case with you not doing what I tell you."

"At least give me some police protection. Somebody to watch my back. That way you'll know who killed me if I fall down on the job."

"We ain't got the manpower to—if the department tried to protect everybody who thinks he's gonna be a victim in New York, we'd need a million men. Ten million."

"Then what the hell am I supposed to do? Just wait around to get killed?"

"Think, that's what. Did you ever think why he's trying to kill you? Because you know who he is, that's why. Or you know something that'd tell me who he is. So why don't you just tell me what you know?"

"I've already told you everything I know. Why don't you tell me everything you know? Maybe it'll fit with what I'm supposed to know."

"I'm not supposed to tell a civilian anything; you're supposed to tell me." Danzig paused for a moment, then said, "OK, here's one thing I found out yesterday. That pitching machine, it has a scale on it. How fast it throws the ball. The one that hit you—it was set for ninety-seven miles an hour."

"That's incredible. There are no pitchers in the game today who can throw that fast. Ryan was once clocked at a hundred and one, but I doubt if he could—"

"Yeah, yeah, but why wasn't it set at the highest speed? I mean, if you're gonna kill a guy, you set it at the most, right?"

"The most? What's the most? What's the highest you could set the machine at?"

"It went from eighty-eight to one seventy-six."

Marc started to laugh, but the motion set his head to ringing. "No one could throw a ball at that velocity. Or hit against it. Or stand up to bat against that speed. If it just touched you, it could break your ribs. It would be too dangerous to keep around. That machine—I was told it's only accurate within about six inches."

"I'm telling you what I read on the scale."

"That scale is set in feet per second, not miles per hour. Eighty-eight feet per second is sixty miles an hour. One seventy-six is one hundred twenty miles an hour. Very, very fast, but acceptable to maybe improve timing.''

"OK, sounds right. Then why was it set at ninety-seven?''

"That's only ten percent more than eighty-eight, which makes it sixty-six miles per hour. A very slow speed.''

"OK, keep talking, I think I got something here. Why a slow speed, if you're trying to kill somebody?''

"It's not really a slow speed; only by comparison to what major league fireball pitchers can do. You can kill somebody at sixty-six miles an hour if you hit him right. The only reason I can think of . . . yes, that has to be it. The killer wasn't taking any chances. If there's a way to determine from the autopsy how hard the ball was thrown, if it showed the ball was thrown at one hundred twenty miles an hour, we'd know it wasn't thrown by a human being. So he set it for a speed that any ballplayer could have thrown it, figuring if he had the opportunity, he'd go in and close the door to the equipment-storage room and later he'd move the machine back and cover it with dust and we'd never know how the murder was committed. Either murder. Prager's and mine. We'd be looking for somebody who *threw* the ball, and never find him, because all the killer had to do was keep his eyes open and press a button at the right time.''

Danzig was quiet for a long time. Finally he said, "You know, Burr, keep thinking—we may come up with something, and hurry up.''

Marc bent over the terminal's keyboard and began typing.

Your reporter has been the victim of two vicious attacks from behind by the murderer of Samuel Moultran Prager because I know who the killer is but I have not yet collected all the evidence the police need to make an arrest. There is one final piece which I expect to obtain shortly after the end of the fourth game of the World Series, and as soon as I have it, I will present the entire file to the proper authorities. To review the facts of the case ...

28

"Mr. Witter's been calling every fifteen minutes," Dahliah announced coldly as soon as Marc came home. "Where were you so late?"

"The hospital emergency room was crowded. Busy day."

"Again? Your head again?" Marc nodded slowly. Very slowly. "Not that I care very much," Dahliah said carefully, "but shouldn't this tell you something? I mean, if you had the intelligence of even a cat, you'd realize that you're, maybe, not really suited for investigative reporting. And, considering the time you've spent in hospitals lately, the hours aren't too good either."

"I'm not *doing* investigative reporting. The murderer's trying to kill me because he doesn't want me to tell Lieutenant Danzig what I know."

"I'm not trying to tell you what to do, you understand, but," Dahliah took a deep breath and hesitated—telling a man he was not very bright was always a chancy thing; some of them got offended very easily—yet there was no other way, "wouldn't it be prophylactic—and maybe save your life, not that I care very much—just to tell Danzig what you know? Then the murderer would have to kill Danzig first and leave you alone." She smiled disarmingly. "Just a suggestion."

It was Marc's turn to breathe deeply; women just didn't understand the most obvious things. "I would gladly tell Danzig what I know but, unfortunately, I don't know anything—about the murder, I mean—that I haven't already told him."

"Maybe it's how you told him. Maybe if you put things in a different order everything would become clear."

"I've thought about it a hundred different ways." He stopped and looked at the empty table. "What's for supper?"

"Anything your little heart desires," Dahliah said expansively. "Just look in the refrigerator. Whatever you find there is yours. But shouldn't you call Mr. Witter now? Do things in the order of their importance? And after you finish talking to him and eating and all the other terribly important things, you can say hello to me. The way you used to do, a year ago. If my memory serves me right."

Marc called. Witter was upset. "Why didn't you phone me after sending in that imbecilic column? Do you really expect me to print it?"

"I was busy. I had to go to the hospital to get my head examined."

"Which I recommended to you some months ago, you may remember, but you didn't take my advice then, so why the rush to do it now? Did you take care of all the important things you volunteered to do?"

"Important things?"

Witter's voice became harsh. "Did you forget that you were supposed to get Lucy Stone Valentine to drop her silly claim of sexual harassment? Against me and, if possible, against *The Sentry?* I wouldn't even mind if she dropped it against you too, provided there is no other way to close the case."

"Well, actually—I'm working on it, Mr. Witter."

"And Nelda Shaver? Did you get her to agree to hand in her copy on Thursday evening, as you swore you would do?"

"I'm still working on that too."

"So you've failed again, Burr, completely."

Why, Marc wondered, did the click of a phone being hung up sound like a death knell?

29

"What's Bello gonna do today?" Dan Zarik asked his coaches.

"He don't have any rabbits left in his hat," Rich Martini said. "Carlson and Androvec are out, and Padilla needs another day's rest minimum. That leaves Muldoon and Lamburt."

"What about if he starts his relievers again? Like in the second game."

"Too risky," Irv Nessen said. "He got away with it by the skin of his teeth last time; didn't have a single good pitcher left if the game went one more inning. Bello don't think like that. He takes chances, sure, when he gotta, but he's always got an out if he gets cornered. My bet is on Lamburt. Between a left-handed fastball and a right-handed knuckleball—hell, we kill fastballs."

"You want to put Grasso in right field," Martini asked, "and Conroy as DH? Give Lamburt a bunch of lefties to face?"

"Nope. Let's keep the batting order the same; we got plenty of lefties. Carter's been doing great and he's real aggressive; sparks the whole team. Keep Grasso at DH. If he don't have fielding to worry about, he does good too."

"Who we gonna pitch?" Nessen asked. "Devine or Harriman?"

"It's Devine's turn, but Harriman did real good the first game and he's plenty rested. I'm going with Harriman. He ain't never gonna pull another bonehead play, you can bet on that. And this time, let's get him some runs. I want all the guys hepped up, see some real aggressive play out there. If the Bandits take us in four, none of us'll get another job again.''

"Ortiz again, Butch?" Verne Sullivan asked.

"Starting relievers worked once, but it ain't gonna work twice. Is Padilla ready? He only pitched three innings."

"Physically, yeah, he's ready, but you know how he is. He don't count innings; he counts days between. Far as he's concerned, he's plumb wore out. Muldoon is fresh and raring to go."

"No way I'm gonna put a left-handed fastball against those guys. Androvec? He pitched less than two innings yesterday."

"Yeah, and at the end of one inning he was already asking for painkillers. Didn't have a long enough warm-up, he said. Another one of Prager's superstars. He's got the wrong attitude for a crucial game; all he thinks about is money."

"You know who that leaves, Verne. And you don't like him either."

"Never did. Goddamn college boy. But he did good in the first game; gotta give him that."

"Think he can do it again? It ain't smart to repeat a trick."

"I got Ortiz ready; he'll be good for two, three innings."

"And after that? Sadoff? Lengo?"

"Never. I been going over the films last night. Throwing a fastball to those gorillas is like throwing a porterhouse to a lion. Nope. If Lamburt and Ortiz can't hold 'em, in goes Androvec and Padilla."

"I thought their attitude wasn't—"

"If I gotta use 'em, I'll change their attitude. With a bat, if talking don't work." He paused for a moment, then said, "I'd like to use Corey Steen for catcher. I know, I know"—he waved aside Bello's objection—"Krumanski's the first-string, but he still ain't throwing right and, besides, Steen's used to catching Lamburt."

"What about shortstop?" Earl Diggins asked. "Rivera or Banneker?"

"If I'm figuring right," Bello said thoughtfully, "it's gonna be another pitchers' battle, so we need the fielding. Go with Pancho. But put Peersen in as DH; might as well get another lefty in the lineup. OK, that's it.'' The coaches got up, ready to leave.

"Wait a minute.'' Verne Sullivan stood up and called the other coaches back. "I got something to say. I know Dan Zarik, played with him and against him for a lot of years. He's smart and he's good, but most of all, he's tough. Just because he's down three games—it don't mean nothing for today. He never gives up. This game is gonna be the roughest one of all and his guys are gonna be chewing rawhide. So your guys, they gotta be tougher, give as good as they get and, whatever it takes, we're gonna win this in four.''

Harriman mowed down the first three Bandits in order.

Lamburt, working slowly, struck out Battles. Carter, crowding the plate, moved out of the way too slowly and took first as a hit batsman. On the third pitch to Cordray, he took off for second. Steen's throw to Rivera was perfect but Carter slid into the little shortstop with his legs high and going like a threshing machine. Rivera dropped the ball and rolled on the ground in agony. The Bandit bench erupted, ready to kill, but Bello waved them back. As Popeye Pitney and his assistant went to Rivera's aid, Bello walked slowly over to Ben Garry, the plate umpire.

Garry had already called Dan Zarik there. "He did that deliberate, Dan,'' Bello said.

"The shortstop was blocking the base path,'' Zarik said. "He had a right. Ask the ump.''

Garry looked hard at Zarik. "It ain't gonna happen again, is it Dan?''

"I never wanted it to happen this way even once,'' Zarik said. "I play hard, not dirty.''

"I'll take your word for it,'' Garry said. "This time.''

"My guys might not be satisfied with that,'' Bello said. "Pancho might never play again, and he got a wife and kids. How you gonna even that out, Dan?''

"What do you want me to do, Butch? Kill Carter?''

"Might not be a bad idea,'' Bello said, and walked away.

Cubby Banneker went in at short, looking angry, just waiting for a Boomer to come his way. Jason Cordray stayed far behind the plate, and seemed more interested in not getting beaned—the traditional reprisal for a spiking—than in hitting the ball. Lamburt struck him out swinging. Big Isaac Brown stood at the plate bravely, and hit a long fly to center field that Rigdale gathered in easily.

As Demarco went to bat in the top of the second, Verne Sullivan turned on Warren Lamburt. "What the hell's the matter with you? You knew what you had to do."

"I never beaned anybody deliberately in my life," Lamburt said quietly, "and I'm not going to start now."

"But Carter deserves it. He's a goddamn animal, a killer. Look what he did to Pancho. That wasn't no accident and you know it."

"Why should I bean Jason Cordray because Carter spikes Rivera?"

"To get even, that's why. To make sure they don't spike Cubby or Joe Kullman or Corey. Because you're *supposed* to. Like a man."

"I'm not going to do it," Lamburt said stubbornly.

"Goddamn college boy," Sullivan muttered and went back to sit with Bello.

"I gotta do something, Butch," Sullivan said. "You can't let this go."

"OK," Bello muttered under his breath, "but only to Carter. Guy like him shouldn't be in baseball."

"Permanent?"

"Is Pancho gonna play again?" Bello asked. Sullivan nodded. "They'll laugh us out of town if we let this go. Take care of it, will you, Verne?"

"I'll tell 'em what to do next time Carter is up," Sullivan said grimly. "Be a lot easier if the college boy wasn't such a goddamn pansy. This way could cost us a run, Butch, but it gotta be done."

Bello thought for a moment, then said, "Whatever happens, happens."

*   *   *

Demarco had struck out, but Reuben Johnson got a single to short right. Harriman, however, got Rigdale on an easy fly and struck out Steen to end the Bandits' half of the inning. In the Boomers' half, Lamburt struck out Casey, and got Hedstrom to ground out. Mel Wheatley got a scratch single, but Blaine hit an easy one to Kullman to force the runner for the third out. No score at the end of the second.

The third inning for the Bandits was a repetition of the first two. Banneker, Peersen, and Kullman went down easily, no runs, no hits, no errors. For the Boomers, Henry Grasso flied out and Sam Battles struck out, bringing up Len Carter. Carter crowded the plate, as usual, daring Lamburt to hit him. Lamburt was taking a very slow windup, but couldn't find the corners and Carter walked. Facing Cordray, Lamburt started taking a slow windup again, and Carter dashed for second. Even though his back was turned, Lamburt, at the signal from the catcher, clumsily stepped off the rubber and threw the ball to Kullman, who was already waiting in front of second base. Carter, running with his head down, slid hard toward the bag, but Kullman slammed his right hand, with the ball in it, into Carter's groin, driving the aluminum cup right up into—as Sullivan had put it when he told them what to do—up into his Adam's apple. Carter screamed and rolled over, curled up, his legs making crawling movements. Slowly he turned over, got up on his knees, and vomited, then collapsed again, into his own vomit.

The Boomer bench emptied out toward second base, but Verne Sullivan, looking ready to kill, was ahead of them. Standing in front of Joe Kullman, he yelled, "Come on, you bastards. You'll get me, but I'll take six of you with me." At this, the Boomers halted, pulled back, and started circling Sullivan and Kullman cautiously, as the Bandits ran up to help their teammates. But the immediate reaction had been short-circuited, so Dan Zarik and Butch Bello were able to get their men back into the dugouts without a major brawl. As Len Carter was carried off on a stretcher, Ben Garry approached the pitcher's mound and beckoned Zarik and Bello to come to him. "That was a balk," Garry said. "The runner advances to second, batter to first."

206

"That's the rules," Bello admitted. "No argument."

"Both you guys ought to be ashamed of yourselves," Garry said. "Millions of kids watching. What're they gonna think?"

"I didn't start it," Bello said.

"I never ordered nobody hurt," Zarik said.

"It ain't gonna happen anymore, boys," Garry said. "Right?"

"Far as I'm concerned," Bello said, "we're even."

Norbert Smalls was put in to run for Carter as Isaac Brown faced Warren Lamburt with two on and two out. With a count of two-and-two, one of Lamburt's knuckleballs came in straight, and Brown parked it in the upper deck of center field to drive in three runs. Lamburt struck out Casey, but the Boomers were leading 3–0 at the end of the third inning.

"That little trick worked too good, Verne," Bello said.

"I wouldn't've had to do it if the college boy done what I told him."

"It cost us three runs, maybe the game. Was it worth it?"

"Sometimes you gotta do what you gotta do, Butch. No matter what it costs."

Alvin Smootra hit a blooper over first for a single and Bob Coffee sent him to second on a neat sacrifice bunt. Mario Demarco poked a single to right that allowed Smootra to score, though he barely beat the throw, but Demarco was held at first. Reuben Johnson hit a long fly to center for the second out. Pete Rigdale waited out a walk, putting two men on with two out, but Corey Steen grounded to third for a force and the Bandits had one run on two hits with two men left on base.

In the Boomers' half, Lamburt made all three batters hit it into the dirt, retiring the side on eight pitched balls. At the end of the fourth inning, the score was 3–1 in favor of the Boomers.

In the fifth, Cubby Banneker started off with a single, but Harriman put down Peersen, Kullman, and Smootra, one, two, three, with no score. Lamburt gave up singles to Battles and Cordray, but ended the inning by striking out Brown, so the score was still 3–1, Boomers.

Coffee hit a single to lead off the sixth inning and Demarco followed with a homer over the right-field fence, tying the score with none out. Taking no chances, Zarik put in right-handed Elias Hook to relieve. Hook got Johnson on a change-up but Pete Rigdale caught a slow curve and doubled to left. Corey Steen fouled off two balls before walking, putting two men on with one out. Bello put in left-handed Yancey Wilder to pinch-hit, but Hook struck out Wilder on four curves. Magee came up with two out and two men on base. He hit Hook's first pitch for a long single to left, sending Steen to second and Rigdale home, to put the Bandits ahead for the first time in the game and bringing up Joe Kullman, the top of the batting order, with two men on and two out. Hook, working carefully, got Kullman to swing at a low change-up and the side was retired.

Lamburt struck out Casey for the third time in a row, but Hedstrom hit a long fly that Rigdale caught with his back against the center-field fence and Wheatley drove a hard one to left field that Coffee barely caught. Three up and three down, but it was clear that the Boomers were beginning to hit Lamburt. At the end of the sixth, the Bandits were leading by a run.

"Pull him now?" Butch asked.

"He's still getting them out," Sullivan said. "Let's see if he got the guts."

"If he's tired, it'll be worse next inning."

"Nobody gets tired throwing knuckleballs; it's a matter of attitude. He got the right attitude, he stays. He folds up, we yank him."

"I didn't know you had that much confidence in Lamburt."

"I don't, but even a dog got to get a chance. Once."

Smootra, Coffee, and Demarco all hit the ball, but were easy outs in the seventh. In the Boomers' half of the inning, Lamburt struck out Blaine. Grasso got a single, but died on base as Battles flied out and Smalls hit into a force at second. Still 4–3, Bandits, at the end of seven.

208

Reuben Johnson started the eighth with a mighty double off the right-field fence, inches away from a home run, and the Bandits' seats went crazy. But Hook, throwing nothing but sharp-breaking curves and sinkers, struck out Rigdale and Steen, and got Willard Madison, who had taken over short from Banneker, to pop up, leaving Johnson on second.

Cordray hit Lamburt's first pitch for a hard drive that went directly into Smootra's glove. Brown hit the third pitch for a very long fly to deep center that Rigdale caught up against the fence. Casey hit a hard grounder between first and second that Kullman barely got to in time. Three up and three down, but a few inches either way and it would have been a rout.

"They're getting to him, Verne." Bello said. "Hard. Next inning they'll kill him."

"We're still ahead."

"Only one run. He screws up, it could mean the Series."

"He knows what he got to do, Butch. Let's see if he does it."

"He don't have the guts. You said so yourself. Even if he has, he ain't gonna stick his neck out. There's maybe more at stake here than the game, you know."

"I know. Let's see if he's a man or a college boy."

"You're taking a big chance with both our lives."

"Won't be the first time, Butch. But I never let you down yet and I never will. You want me to pull him now, you tell me."

Bello thought for a second, then said, "No. I trust your judgment. You pull him when you're ready. I'll take the flak if we're wrong."

"I'll know by the first pitch."

Elias Hook, covered with sweat and concentrating on every pitch, worked the corners like a surgeon and struck out Peersen, Kullman, and Smootra. Even the Brooklyn side gave him an admiring hand, though grudgingly.

Catcher Herb Hedstrom, a right-handed batter, was the first man to face Warren Lamburt in the crucial inning of what might be the deciding game of the World Series. Lamburt wound up and threw a perfect strike right down the middle just above the knees at ninety-five miles an hour, exactly as he had done in the old days, when, at the age of twenty, he had been the Boy Wonder of baseball. Hedstrom, in shock, all set for a knuckleball, didn't take the bat off his shoulders. Lamburt followed this up with another fastball, this time over the inside corner. His timing thrown completely off, Hedstrom swung weakly at the ball, much too late. Not knowing what to expect now, he dug in, but the third pitch was a change-up and he was called out on strikes.

Desperate, Zarik called on Hale Porter to pinch-hit for Wheatley. Porter was a left-handed batter, but was the only reliable power hitter Zarik had left. Porter was prepared to connect with a knuckleball, but Lamburt fed him two fastballs, low and inside, coming across the plate to a left-handed batter, and struck him out on a sinker. Blaine beat out a bunt on the first pitch and Grasso waited out a three-and-two count and walked.

Battles, the last man who had a chance to save the Boomers, was a right-handed batter, vindicating Verne Sullivan's strategy. For the first pitch, Lamburt gave Battles a knuckler that floated lazily across the plate. Battled started to swing, then pulled back. Strike one. The next pitch was a change-up that Battles was completely unprepared for. He swung at it weakly, the timing so far off that, had he connected, it would have been no better than a pop fly. Warren Lamburt wound up quickly for the next pitch, a fast, sharp-breaking curve cutting diagonally across the inside corner that Battles instinctively jumped away from. The umpire's hand was up. Strike three! Out! The game was over; the Bandits had won! The Bandits had *WON!* Won the game and won the World Series. *THE WORLD SERIES!* In four straight! From the mighty Jersey Boomers! The Bandits were the new World Champions!

It was unbelievable. Marc shook his head in wonderment. Inconceivable. Yet it had happened. It had just happened, in front of his eyes. This was what Marc loved about sports, the unpredictability, the upsets, the underdogs winning, the randomness—no, it was not really random. It was the spirit, the desire, the drive that made champions out of ordinary human beings, that made ordinary humans extraordinary, godlike, that gave hope to the millions, the billions, who fought against the odds in their lives and beat them, that recognized and glorified those who beat the odds, that inspired others to fight and to keep fighting so that, though most never made it, sometimes, once in a while, the last would be first.

He bent over his keyboard to firm up these words for a special column—he would *make* Julius Witter print it tomorrow—to give hope to those who, by all odds, should have no hope but hoped nevertheless, to show them that they too could win, if they tried.

Then he stopped. He knew. He didn't want to know, but he knew. Who had killed Samuel Moultran Prager. Not only who, but also what, where, when, why, and how. The reporter's catechism. Everything. So clear. So simple. And now he had to do something about it. He didn't want to do something about it, he didn't want to do *anything* about it, but he had no choice. There had to be a way to take care of things so that . . . not to really *avoid* the pain—it was too late for that—but to reduce . . . wasn't that the whole point of . . . ? He had to do this himself. Quietly. Nicely. With dignity. Man to man. Reason together. Privately. After the crowd thinned out a bit. But before Danzig got there.

He bent over the keyboard again and started typing. But he couldn't see very well; his eyes were too full.

30

"OK, they're all gone now," Butch Bello said patiently. "What's so important you had to talk to me about?" They were sitting in the visiting team's locker room, the Bandits' locker room, surrounded by champagne bottles and flung papers and thrown uniforms, all in a joyous mess.

"I—" Marc said, hesitantly, "that is, I have a problem." Bello waited. "But first, let me tell you how much I admire your brilliance as a manager. I don't think any other manager in baseball could have pulled off the miracle you did. Four straight over the Boomers. The greatest upset in history."

"Yeah, well, there was a lot of luck to it too. And the Bandits are not as bad a team as you guys made us out, especially in the columns. Including you. Now what's your problem? My wife is waiting for me."

"Danzig, Lieutenant Danzig, is coming here to arrest me. For the murder of Mr. Prager."

"That's crazy. You didn't kill Prager."

"I know that and you know that. I'm sure even Danzig knows that. But he's got to arrest *somebody*, and if it can't be the real killer, he's going to arrest me. And by the time he gets through with me, I'll confess to half the killings in Brooklyn. Jersey too."

"I'm sorry to hear that, Burr, but what has that got to do with me? How the hell can I help you?"

"You can help me by . . ." Marc looked straight at Butch Bello.

"Well, first of all, I know you didn't mean to kill me. You didn't even mean to hit me. With the pitching machine, that is. You aimed it for above my head. It just happened to hit me because it's only accurate within about six inches. Luckily for me, you had set it at low speed. Purposely, I guess. So it shouldn't hurt me if it did hit me accidentally. Just in case."

"You know, Burr, I'm glad you're all right, even though, sometimes, to tell the truth, I felt like killing you, you and all the other reporters, that is, who were giving me a hard time in the papers. But I don't like what you're telling me now. Why me?"

"I just want to show you there are no hard feelings, Butch. Honest. I like you and I really respect you. You understand? Like when I was in the press box. You could have come closer, thrown the ball really hard, killed me. You could even have hit me with a bat. Made sure. Come up right behind me. The floors are carpeted. I'd never have heard you."

"Only a dope would carry a bat to the pressroom. If somebody saw you, how the hell would you explain it?"

"Yes, well, still . . . The point is, I didn't understand then that the killer *wasn't* trying to kill me. That he didn't want to hurt me, wasn't even trying to hit me. He just wanted me to write about, tell the police about, balls being thrown at my head to kill me because I knew too much. I didn't know too much. I didn't know anything. The whole point of hitting me in the head was to focus attention on a beanball, to get the idea across that Prager was killed by a beanball."

"He wasn't?"

"No. You see, the killer—you—wanted to make sure that no one—not just you, but no one—could be accused of killing Prager. You didn't want any of your players, or your coaches, or anybody, to have a hard time because you killed Prager. Which was very decent—just what I would have expected of you."

"That don't sound like a hell of a compliment. You're accusing me of killing Prager?"

"Yes, well, when I saw that last game . . . You had a lot of guts

213

to leave Lamburt in for the whole game, gambling that he would throw his fastball in the last of the ninth, and maybe ruin his arm forever, just when he had another five years in the majors, maybe more, as a knuckleball pitcher.''

"You got to give Verne Sullivan credit for that. He figured it out, he had the faith. And Lamburt. I thought he was soft, but he had the brains to know what to do and the balls to do it. If he wants to, if his arm is gone, he can be a coach for me as long as he wants.''

"For a while, I thought that maybe Verne Sullivan . . . he'd do anything for you, Butch. Anything. The trouble is—what I mean—I don't think you'll be managing . . . you really should give yourself up. That's the best way. I've figured it all out. Not to Danzig—God forbid. He'll put on the pressure and when you crack he'll take you downtown and sweat you and put you in a cell with . . . And after you confess, he'll read you the Miranda and . . . that's the way he works. He doesn't know any other way. And he's got the best record in . . . they haven't caught him at it yet. No, definitely not Danzig. What you should do is get a good lawyer and have him make a deal with the D.A. Temporary insanity. You plead temporary insanity. If the guy who shot the president . . . Under those conditions, with Prager . . . I'll testify for you.''

"I don't need nobody to tell me I'm crazy. You're crazy if you think I'm going to say I killed Prager. I was nowhere near where . . . Forget it—I'm going home.''

"No, not yet. Don't go yet. Listen to me. Then, if you want to, then you can go home. When Danzig arrests me, I'll have to tell him what I know. Then he'll arrest you and . . It won't hurt you to stay another few minutes, hear what I have to tell Danzig. Maybe I'm making a mistake, maybe I got it all wrong. Show me where I'm wrong and I won't tell Danzig.''

"I'll listen,'' Bello said, not very patiently, "but let's start walking. There's only one gate left open at this time and it's a long way from here.''

They got up and started walking slowly, Marc carrying his computer terminal, Bello with his little equipment bag. "In the beginning of the game today," Marc said, "when Len Carter spiked Pancho Rivera, that's when I knew. Only I didn't know I knew. Actually, it was only the next time Carter came up, when Joe Kullman got even with him—"

"Lamburt should've beaned the next batter. That's the way it should've been done, the way it's always been done."

"Yes, well, lucky for me it wasn't. Because when Kullman slammed the ball into Carter's groin, it all became clear. Not at the moment, my mind wasn't on the murder then, but later, when the game was over. Prager wasn't hit by a thrown ball. What happened was . . . you didn't actually plan it, but when the opportunity arose, you took advantage of the situation. Like a good manager. On the spur of the moment. And your follow-up was just as brilliant. The same qualities that make a good manager, make a successful murderer."

"More of your back-assed compliments, Burr?"

"It's true. Prager called you and told you he wanted to meet you in your office, privately, to give you the game plan, tell you how to run the team. Exactly. In detail. So he wouldn't have to phone down to you so much in the middle of the game. That way, you could take the blame if anything went wrong and he could take the credit for anything that went right. Typical Prager maneuver. So you met at noon, when you told Verne Sullivan you were getting your yogurt. Prager told you what he wanted. You knew that if you followed Prager's play-it-safe ideas, you'd lose the game, the whole Series. In four straight. You knew that the only chance you had was to surprise the Boomers, to use unconventional strategies, but you knew too that the moment Prager saw what was going on, he would countermand your orders, and would even fire you in the middle of the game, if he thought it was necessary. This was your only chance at a World Championship, and your only chance to stay in baseball, if it came down to it. So, for the championsnip, for your dreams, for the *team*, you decided to kill Prager. To get him out of your office quickly, you swore to do everything he told you. Prager, himself, didn't want to be seen talking to you either; if the Bandits lost the game, he'd be able to say he had nothing to do with it. So you opened the waiting-room door, stood in the recess and peeked out to see if anyone was in the passage or looking into the passage. No one was. As you were talking, you were putting on your batting gloves, casually. You now had the ball in your right hand. You let Prager out. As he stepped into the recess, you grabbed him by his suit collar with your left hand and slammed the ball into the right side of his head. Maximum velocity of a pitch is the instant the ball is released; after that, the air resistance slows it down. So with a speed of maybe ninety miles an hour, you slammed the ball into his head. Crushing it. Killing him. Still holding on to his collar, you peeked out again. Still no one there. You dropped the body just outside the recess and continued out, taking off your gloves as you walked. Calmly. To meet me.''

Bello looked troubled. ''And you want me to tell all this to Danzig? Even if I did what you said, and I ain't admitting nothing, why should I? Even if I got off, with insanity, you think I'd ever manage again? Forget it, Burr.''

''If you don't, Butch, I will. Even if I don't want to, I'll have to. He'll make me.''

''No he won't,'' Bello said grimly, and reached for Marc. Marc reacted with a gymnast's speed, throwing his terminal into Butch's belly, and ran. Butch kept walking slowly, and unzipped his little bag. ''No use, Burr. I took you the wrong way. The exit's in the other direction. In a minute, you'll come to a gate. They divide up the areas from each other for security. With big gates. I discovered that yesterday. We just passed the last fire exit. It's a dead end, Burr; no way out.'' He took a baseball from his bag. ''I'll wipe off the prints later.''

''Don't do it, Butch,'' Marc pleaded, running backward. ''Danzig will be here any minute. You'll be caught.''

''If I am''—Bello threw the ball, hard; Marc ducked in time and the ball bounced off a wall—''I'm no worse off than before. But they won't let him in.'' He reached into the bag and got another ball.

216

"Then you can't get out. They'll find you in here with my body."

"No they won't." Bello threw again. He was getting closer. "I'll go out by the fire exit. They'll know the killer left that way, but they won't know who. And this'll convince 'em Prager was killed by a beanball." He got another ball out of the bag and kept stalking Marc.

Marc turned and ran as fast as he could. In a few moments he came to a big metal grille that closed the corridor completely. It was heavy, immovable. Marc turned, his back against it. Bello was within sixty feet of him now. The burly manager threw the ball, not aiming at Marc's head this time, just trying to disable him for the final beanball. Marc dived sideways, just in time. Desparately, he ran toward Bello at full speed. At the last second he launched himself upward and forward, in a tight double forward somersault, fully tucked in, his body rotating like a buzz saw. When Bello saw the whirling juggernaut coming, he instinctively braced his legs, put his head down with his left shoulder forward, as he had done so many times in his career as a catcher when a runner was trying to make home past him.

Just as Marc was about to smash into Bello, his head exploded in a brilliant, blinding white flash.

31

"They're all here now," Dahliah said softly.

Marc opened one eye and squinted sideways. Hospital rooms all had the same cool green look; you couldn't tell which one you were in without a scorecard. "Tell them to get close to the side of the bed, where I can see them." He opened the other eye. No improvement.

"Why are you lying face down?" Nelda Shaver asked. "Why don't you just turn over?"

"Because the left side of my head has a big lump on it and it hurts."

"So turn on the right side."

"That side has a lump too."

"Humor him," Julius Witter said. "I still have use for whatever information is locked in that skull. I missed a good story this afternoon because he foolishly insisted on getting clobbered again without my authorization and even now, my own reporter—assistant editor, actually—is in the hospital and *The Sentry* doesn't have any more facts than the other papers. It's humiliating. Worse than that"—Witter looked at his watch—"it's getting very close to deadline, Burr. Do you want *The Sentry* to miss tomorrow's headlines too because you stubbornly refused to come out of your coma for two whole hours?"

"I have an important appointment," Lucy Valentine complained. "Why do I have to be here? This isn't news for 'The Sporting Woman.' "

"Burr wouldn't talk until you got here too," Lieutenant Danzig said. "If it'd make you feel better," he added helpfully, "I could always hold you as a material witness."

"The more you complain," Dahliah said, "the longer it will take to get out of here and leave me alone with him."

"I'll start with you, Miss Valentine," Marc said. "Do you still intend to bring suit against me for sexual harassment?" Witter raised a finger as a reminder. "And against Mr. Witter and *The Sentry*?"

"Against *you*?" Dahliah was shocked. "You? I thought that Witter . . . *you* did it?"

"Yes. No! Certainly not. I was the one she . . . but I didn't. I wouldn't."

"You did," Valentine said smugly. "In front of witnesses. My appointment tonight is with a lawyer."

"Exactly, Miss Valentine. In front of witnesses. I was thinking about it when I was waiting for—after the game. When you see your lawyer, ask him, her, if . . . give him these facts, first." Marc drew a deep breath, and winced. There were four places on his head that were pounding now, each at a slightly different time. Like a quadruple whammy, but real. "I was standing at the far side of the field when you came. You walked to me across the entire infield while a practice was going on."

"It was the shortest way," Lucy explained.

"You're not supposed to go on the field when . . . You tell her, Julius."

"It is extremely dangerous. You could have been killed by a thrown ball or, worse, a batted ball. Since you were there voluntarily, in disregard of all custom and usage in the sport, you would not have been covered by our insurance and possibly not by theirs either. It's called contributory negligence. Further, you could have distracted a player so that he got hit or injured himself. In which case their insurance company would have sued *The Sentry*. And won. Some of these players are worth millions of dollars to their teams. Tens of millions."

"How was I supposed to know that?" Lucy said.

"A sports reporter who doesn't know these elementary things?" Witter raised his eyebrows. "Miss Valentine, you astound me. Don't you read in your spare time? Study? However did you hope to become a permanent member of our team?"

"That's not all," Marc said. "You were wearing a very tight red dress when you crossed the field, and no bra."

"How I dress is my business," she snapped.

Witter sighed. "How you dress is certainly your business, Miss Valentine. But when you cross a baseball field on which there are a hundred young, healthy athletes working, anything you do that helps distract their attention is not just your business. If I sent you into a locker room and you wore a—for example—a G-string and nothing else, your professional judgement might reasonably be questioned, as well as your fitness for induction into our hallowed profession. I have a feeling that, under the circumstances, your attorney will want a substantial sum as a retainer."

"That's not all." Marc took up the cudgels. "The first thing you did was throw your arms around me and hold me closely and tightly. And blow in my ear and nibble on it."

"I did not. I just told you to hand over the film."

"There are a hundred witnesses who saw what you did, and not one of them heard what you just said you said. And right after that, did you not hold me even closer? And wiggle against me, rub against me provocatively?"

"I was just trying to get you to give me the film."

"Ask the hundred witnesses; see what they say. If you only wanted the film, why didn't you just hold out your hand? A friendly handshake would have accomplished the job quickly and easily. Or were you trying to set up a situation where you could put Mr. Witter into a compromising position?"

"I can't help how men act. They all lie for each other."

"One hundred men? Rivals for the World Championship? The heroes of America?" Marc smiled, even though it hurt. "Mr. Witter, do you really think Miss Valentine shows enough interest in

220

sports, and has the appropriate professional attitude for our great journal?''

"I'm afraid not. I really went out of my way to obtain a good woman for *The Sentry*, but it is clear that you, Miss Valentine, lack even the slightest promise of becoming a competent sports journalist.''

"An intern," Valentine said, "is supposed to be kept on for six months.''

"Ah, yes," Witter said, "I see you've been reading the fine print. However, a reporter—to which position you, ah, persuaded me to promote you, is, on *The Sentry*, on probation for ninety days, during which time he may be excessed for cause. In your case, Miss Valentine, I think the cause is more than sufficient. Nelda, since you are her direct supervisor, would you do the honors?''

In her extreme pleasure, Nelda Shaver risked a full half-smile. "Miss Valentine, my dear Lucy, you are fired. With prejudice. Don't bother using me for a reference. Or claiming discrimination. You may leave now. And don't slam the door; this is a hospital, you know.''

Lucy Valentine tossed her head. Marc couldn't help noticing she was still not wearing a bra. "I don't care," she said. "You haven't heard the end of this. I'm going to write up this whole incident and take it to *Ms.*''

"A good idea," Nelda said. "Do that little thing. But keep in mind that there's one little difference between you and Gloria Steinem: She's got brains.'' Lucy stormed out. Nelda turned back to Marc. "Thank you, dear. That was very neatly done. It will be an even greater pleasure working with you than I had hoped.''

"Now wait a minute," Dahliah said, "I don't want—''

"It's all right, Dahliah," Marc broke in. "I've been thinking about it too. Unfortunately, I can't work with you, Nelda, delightful as that might have been. My duties as assistant editor and reporter and columnist take so much of my time, it would be impossible to do the job justice.''

"But I still need an editor. Julie told me a month ago that he could no longer do the work, and he promised me someone nice to work with.''

"A month ago? Mr. Witter, a *month* ago? Someone *nice*?''

"Well, as it happens . . . you know, my boy, I always had the intention of . . . and when the opportunity arose . . . with your best interests at heart, of course. You *had* earned a raise.''

"Well, actually, Nelda,'' Marc said, "what I had in mind is that you still give us your page on Thursday close for editing on Friday.''

"Dear Marc, I *am* very grateful to you for getting rid of that scheming little—young lady, but I've already explained to you how *upset* Mr. Heisenberg would be if—''

"Mr. Heisenberg will be very pleased when he sees how much his revenues have risen when we publish your page in the Saturday edition. The Monday sports edition will always sell well because the men need a tabloid to read on the way to starting a week's work. Takes their mind off the horrors of a new week. But the Saturday paper, poor orphan, has only half the circulation of the other days' papers. With your page in it, the women will buy the Saturday paper, and therefore the advertisers will buy space and Mr. Heisenberg will be overjoyed.''

"Well, actually''—Nelda was thinking hard—"yes, I wouldn't mind being the star of the Saturday edition, but there's one teensy-weensy little problem. Most of the dirt in my gossip—that is, in the personal-news box—is made on the weekend. My readers don't want to know what happened *last* week. It would just *kill* them. Besides, maybe by next week, who did what with whom will be a dead issue; some of these types change partners practically *daily*.''

"I've thought of that too, Nelda, don't worry. You'll have *two* latest-dirt spots; one in the Saturday paper and another, just the box, in the Monday sports section.''

"Ooh, I like that. Marc, you're a dear, dear boy and as soon as you get out of the hospital and we start working together, I'll . . .''

She saw Dahliah's face, and turned to Julius Witter. "You do agree, don't you, Julie? I know Mr. Heisenberg will be so pleased when I tell him.''

"Hmmm, well, it seems to be an acceptable solution to . . . Yes, I don't see why not. It may mean a bit more work for Marc, but he's young and strong and—"

"No it won't Julius. We're going to hire a warm body, remember?"

"That was in case . . . surely you remember the circumstances? If, I said, *if* there were to be a vacancy?"

"There is a vacancy, Julius. You have just saved the salary of a reporter. Miss Valentine, remember? I wonder what it was she said to you, or promised you, that made you promote her so quickly? Well, I suppose I could always call her to find out, but that won't be necessary, will it, Julius? Would you believe that Dahliah was going to introduce her to two lawyers, women lawyers, who were going to take the case for nothing and who specialize in . . . ? But that's no longer pertinent, is it, Julius?"

"What, exactly, did you have in mind, Burr?"

"A promising young, very handsome, journalism student, assigned to Nelda. One with experience editing the school paper. Someone who will be compatible with the requirements of the position. Compatibility is terribly important when two people have to work closely together, don't you agree? If you're too busy, Nelda will help you select the proper candidate."

"That's a very good idea, Marc." Nelda nodded carefully. "Really. But my Saturday and Monday boxes, the gossip—he'll have to be someone who understands the way I work."

"You can explain his duties to him when you're interviewing the applicants. Which may take some time but I'm sure that eventually you'll find the one who'll fill your requirements."

"OK now, enough of this crap," Danzig said. "I've been listening to this fancy waltzing around long enough, and I'm getting tired. Witter convinced me not to take you in for murder while you was unconscious, but so far I didn't hear nothing to change my mind."

"Murder?" Marc lifted his head and felt the beginnings of another brilliant, blinding white—and dropped his forehead back on the pillow fast. "I didn't kill Prager and you know it."

"Maybe you did and maybe you didn't," Danzig growled. "I'm talking about the murder of Enzo Bello, former manager of the Brooklyn Bandits. Who you killed."

"Me? Killed? Are you crazy? He was trying to kill me."

"Yeah? That ain't the way I seen it. You killed him with a karate kick."

"You saw . . . ? You were *there*? Then why didn't you protect me?"

"I tried to protect you, but you were too fast for me. Now I don't want to hear no more bullshit. Why did you kill him?"

"Wait a minute, Danzig, wait a minute. There's something funny going on. You were there when Butch was trying to kill me? You tried to protect me but I was too fast for you? Too fast for what? How?"

"Are you gonna talk, Burr, or not? Cause if you ain't—"

"Sure I'll talk. To my lawyer. Julius, get *The Sentry*'s lawyer over here fast. I'm not saying another word until—"

"Hey, kid, you don't have to be so like that. We don't need no lawyers, do we? We're old friends. Didn't I take you to the best diner in Brooklyn?"

"What happened, Danzig?"

"Well, I was a little delayed—couldn't get there right after the game, see, and—"

"You mean you wanted the murderer to have a chance at me in privacy?"

"Yeah, well, that too, a little. I mean, you didn't turn nothing up in almost a week, the case was getting cold, and I got lots of other cases, so . . . I got there in time to save your life, didn't I?"

"When did you get there?"

"Don't forget, the security guards, bunch of dumb amateurs, they wouldn't let me in so fast. First they had to call the supervisor and he had to check my badge."

"When, Danzig?"

"When you and Bello was walking. Almost finishing walking."

"Why didn't you say something, then? Don't bother," Marc said wearily, "I know. You were trying to hear what we were saying."

"Well, sure, that's very important. If I sweat a guy and he screams for a lawyer, anything he tells me, the D.A. can't use. But if I happen to hear something, accidental like, that counts. I wouldn't expect an amateur like you to know that, but that's OK. I could live with it."

"So you were following us, trying to hear what we were saying."

"Surveillance, it's called. A good cop knows how to do it. Trouble is, the concrete floors—he could've heard my footsteps if I got too close. They call us detectives 'gumshoes' but that ain't accurate. Not modern detectives. And the echoes from the concrete walls . . . it's very hard to make out what's being—"

"So when he tried to kill me, why didn't you do something? Shoot him?"

"Hey, that was a favor, kid. Remember the last time? When you told me not to shoot the perpetrator? I did it for you."

"You were willing to let him kill me?"

"Well, it would've been an airtight case. Right in front of a police officer. But I gave up the case, a solid case, just to protect you."

"You gave up . . . ? Why? How did you protect me?"

"When I saw you was going to use karate on him, I knew it wouldn't be a solid case, so I—there was baseballs all over the hall and—"

"Why didn't you grab him? From behind?"

"You see how big he was? It's been a long time since . . . and you didn't want me to use my gun, so . . ."

"You threw a baseball at him? You killed him yourself?"

"Well, no. Not exactly. Like I said, it's been a couple of years since—"

"You hit *me,* you bastard. That's why my head hurts. You missed him twice and hit me? Twice? Once on each side?"

"No, honest, just once. I only picked up one ball. I had to keep one hand free, in case I had to use the gun."

"In case he went after you, you mean."

"Well, sure. You didn't say I shouldn't use a gun to protect myself, did you?"

"Then how did I get both sides of my head . . . ?"

"Well, after you killed Bello, you was sort of unconscious, and when you fell down . . . the concrete . . . see, you didn't fall right, even though you told me once you was an expert in falling down."

"I was sort of unconscious because you hit me with . . . oh, forget it. Just tell me, if I was unconscious, how did I kill Bello?"

"He was standing sort of sideways with his head down and you was going around so fast and your feet caught his head and . . . what are you asking me for? You're the expert with the karate; I'm just expert with a gun."

"It wasn't karate, it was gymnastics. A simple forward . . . a double flip."

"Yeah, that's what I mean. A new karate kick, both feet. Never seen that one before, not even on TV."

"What I think"—Marc's voice was muffled as he tried, still face down, to turn his head into the pillow in a more comfortable position—"is that you're an accessory to the death of Butch Bello, the most popular man in Brooklyn as of right now. And if you think you can pin this on me, you're even stupider than I think you are."

"Now wait a minute, Burr. I saved your life, just remember that. And I still got you on the withholding-evidence charge."

"Good. Let's get the D.A. up here and we'll both explain everything to him."

Julius Witter coughed expressively. "I think I may have a solution which will satisfy all our requirements. You don't really need the credit for solving the murder of Mr. Prager, do you, Marc my boy? And with Lieutenant Danzig as a witness, the death of Mr. Bello—who is so famous today that any D.A. would be happy to prosecute even the weakest case—the unfortunate *accidental* death of Mr. Bello as he attacked our brave reporter, who, while working hand-in-hand with Lieutenant Danzig . . . you see?"

"I want it in writing. Witnessed by you."

"Of course, my boy. Now all we need is a complete description of how . . . I just happen to have a tape recorder handy."

"Not necessary. Dahliah, call the *Post*, *The Times*, the *News*, and *Newsday*. Press conference in half an hour."

"Marc, you ungrateful little wretch, have you no loyalty?"

"Sure. That's why it's only going to cost *The Sentry* fifty a week."

"I've already explained to you that editors do not get paid extra for news stories."

"You can have the news story at the same time as the others, free. What I'm selling is exclusive rights to my personal experience. As told by the victim."

"But fifty a week? Are you crazy?"

"Is there a limit on what an editor can get for a raise?"

"Certainly not. An editor is management."

"That's what I thought. Fifty for the story and another fifty for the problems I solved and the anguish caused by your poor choice of interns."

"Another fifty? For the problems?"

"You're getting away cheap. What would you have paid a lawyer for Valentine alone? And if you don't like paying for the story, how about fifty per concussion? Combat pay?"

"Very well, one hundred total, but one of these days, the tables will be turned, Burr. Then we shall see who laughs last." He placed the tape recorder on the table next to Marc's bed. "You may start now."

"I want ten minutes with Dahliah first."

"Five. I'm holding a thousand words open and it's very late. I have no desire to pay overtime to the lower classes. Come, Danzig."

As soon as the door closed, Marc whispered to Dahliah, "While I'm dictating, tell the doctor to come in and swear, in front of Witter, that I have to have a week's rest due to multiple concussions or something. Make that two weeks. We'll use the vacation to get married and go on a honeymoon. We can afford to get married now, and I really love you."

"That's very sweet, Marc, and I love you too, but . . ."

"But . . . ?"

"I've already spoken to the doctor. You're not allowed to exert yourself in any way, and especially not to move your head. A honeymoon with an immobile husband is not exactly what every girl dreams of. You really have had multiple concussions, and you're going to have to spend the next week in the hospital, under observation.''

"Are you kidding? Like this?"

"When your head stops hurting, they'll let you turn over."

"Great. And when I do?"

"We'll see." She kissed him lightly. "You still owe me an anniversary present, remember? Maybe I'll collect then."